Jepson Prairie
Preserve
Handbook
3rd Edition

Jepson Prairie Docent Program

Carol W. Witham & Kate Mawdsley, Editors

2012

© 2012 **Jepson Prairie Docent Program**

ISBN: 978-0-9882593-0-0

c/o Solano Land Trust
1001 Texas Street, Suite C
Fairfield, CA 94533

Drafting, design, and printing of this handbook was made possible by generous support of the National Park Service Challenge Cost Share Program.

Contents

Introduction

Jepson Prairie Preserve is one of California's best remaining examples of claypan vernal pools and bunchgrass prairie. These habitats were once more widespread in the great central valley, but most have been converted to agriculture and development. Jepson Prairie was acquired by The Nature Conservancy in 1980 to protect this increasingly scarce remnant of California landscape. In 1997 it was transferred to the Solano Land Trust to place continuing land management responsibilities in local hands. Research and educational use has been administered through the University of California, Davis, Natural Reserve System since 1983.

Vernal pools are temporary bodies of water. They form where an impermeable layer prevents rainwater from percolating downward though the soil. Depressions in this landscape form shallow seasonal pools. The pools dry completely in summer. Many animals and plants have evolved unique strategies to deal with the annual extremes of flood and drought. Due to scarcity of this habitat, a number of Jepson Prairie's vernal pool species are listed under the federal or state Endangered Species Act.

The mounds and other slightly more elevated areas of the Preserve contain bunchgrass prairie. Purple Needlegrass, Bluegrass and Melic Grass are among the native perennial species which form extensive stands at Jepson Prairie.

The editors hope that this handbook, more colorful and reader-friendly than the 1989 and 1998 editions, will find a wide audience among visitors and others who wish to learn more about the fascinating environment of vernal pool grasslands. The Jepson Prairie Docents encourage and invite you to share our appreciation of this precious remnant of historic California.

– Geographic Setting

The map at right shows the geographical setting of Jepson Prairie. The towns are labeled for reference, and the landscape features show how Jepson Prairie fits into and interacts with the region's ecology. Soils and water plus climate shape the ecology of Jepson Prairie.

Soils: The soils at Jepson Prairie are derived from sedimentary rocks, primarily sandstone, originating in the Vaca Mountains to the west. The oldest alluvial fans in the Jepson area were deposited 60 to 100 thousand years ago, before the last cycle of glaciation in the Sierra Nevada. Through thousands of years' worth of precipitation, the soils have weathered into heavy clay that is both alkaline and saline. In places, the claypan is at or near the surface. The poor soils are responsible for the site's undisturbed preservation today. They are not very fertile and are difficult to cultivate.

Water: Rainfall played a significant role in the formation of soils at Jepson Prairie and is critical to the plants and animals of vernal pools.

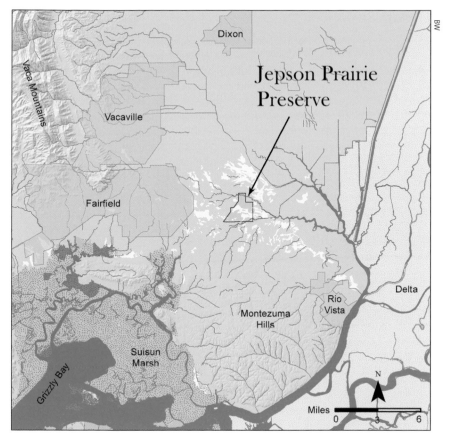

Geographic setting of Jepson Praurie Preserve.

When there is too much rainfall, water moves downslope into tributaries of larger aquatic systems. Jepson Prairie sits on a low ridge between the Sacramento and San Joaquin River Delta system and the Suisun Marsh. Excess rainfall from the Jepson Prairie eventually flows into the Delta via Barker Slough or Calhoun Cut, at the north and south ends of the Preserve, respectively. However, because the ridge is slightly bowed, excess rainfall on parcels only a couple miles west of the Preserve flows into the San Francisco Bay via the Suisun Marsh.

Climate: Most of California has a Mediterranean climate which is characterized by mild wet winters and hot dry summers. The growing season in the Jepson Prairie area is winter and spring. Plants germinate with the first significant storm, usually in late October. For most of the plants on the Preserve, which are annuals, the growing season ends in about late May. The plants must grow and set seed in this short season. But the season is even shorter for some of the vernal pool animals that rely on the water in the vernal pools.

History of Jepson Prairie

The great central valley of California lies between the Coast Ranges on the west and the Sierra Nevada on the east. Winter flooding was formerly common from the several river systems which cross the valley on their way to the Pacific Ocean; it is now controlled by dams and levee systems. Rice fields, tomatoes, and cities cover what was once a rich mosaic of wildflower fields, bunchgrass prairie, vernal pools, freshwater marsh, and riparian forest.

For many centuries before Europeans came to the valley in the early 1800s, the Wintun Native Americans had several small villages near Jepson Prairie and used it for hunting and gathering seeds and bulbs. A few of their arrow points and grinding stones have been found at the edge of Olcott Lake.

Native Americans at Jepson Prairie

Native Americans lived in the Jepson Prairie area since before 1500 BCE. Village sites with burials and fragments of stone pestles, shell beads, obsidian, parts of baskets and bone fishhooks from this era have been found nearby. The tribelets are identified as southern Wintun, part of a much larger group which occupied the Sacramento Valley. In the rich and productive areas near Jepson Prairie, the Wintun lived as hunter-gatherers.

There is no evidence that there was ever a village on Jepson Prairie. However, the Wintun might have come to the playa pools to hunt visiting waterfowl in winter. Obsidian arrow points and classic plummet charmstones (see below) have been found there. Tule elk were available in the neighboring sloughs. Women used basketry sieves to strain protein-rich aquatic invertebrates from the playa pools to be dried and pounded into paste. Native Americans also collected and ground several types of seeds for flour. Late-summer burning of the grasslands promoted both the large-seeded annuals and the bunchgrasses. The bulb plants such as brodiaea were dug up, then the bulblets replanted, while the large bulbs were taken to be roasted or boiled. For example see Dwarf Brodiaea (page 46).

CWW

Charmstones or plummets, much like the one in this photo, have been found in and around the large vernal pools at Jepson Prairie. One theory is that they were weights on throwing nets, which were used to capture flocks of waterfowl.

Jepson Prairie Through Time

By the 1880s, the large native grazers had been replaced by cattle and sheep, and the Native Americans had been driven from the region or killed by smallpox and other newly introduced diseases. The gold rush was over, and agriculture had become well established in the valley. The heavy alkaline clay soils of Jepson Prairie saved it from being leveled, plowed, and planted with crops; the land was much better suited to livestock grazing.

As the population of California continued to grow in the late 1800s, roads and railroads began to appear in this part of the valley. The Sacramento Northern's 90-mile line from the Key System ferry pier in Oakland to Sacramento opened in 1913. It passed through the grasslands of Solano County with a stop at Dozier Station, which is at the north boundary of Jepson Prairie Preserve. Eucalyptus trees were planted on about 500 acres in a failed attempt to produce wood for furniture.

The now abandoned Sacramento Northern Railroad tracks are visible behind a small vernal pool filled with Fringed Downingia (page 50).

Power and gas lines followed the roads and railroads, and development accelerated with California's population explosion after World War II. Scientists began to realize that only fragments of California's original 13 million acres of grassland remained and that undisturbed vernal pools were also becoming critically rare. Researchers at the University of California (UC) had long used the area as a field site and were very aware of its importance as a habitat for rare species. In 1959 a new species, Solano Grass (*Tuctoria mucronata*), was discovered on the dry bed of Olcott Lake. This grass has since been found only in two other nearby locations. In the mid-1970s a preservation committee was organized to protect the grassland and vernal pool communities in the Dozier Station region. From the start, it was obvious that Olcott Lake took top priority for preservation, since at the time it was the only known habitat not only for the Solano Grass, but for the equally rare Delta Green Ground Beetle (*Elaphrus viridis,* see page 30).

On December 31, 1980 The Nature Conservancy (TNC) purchased 1,566 acres of property containing Olcott Lake and surrounding bunchgrass prairie from the Southern Pacific Railroad. A major portion of the purchase price was contributed to TNC by an anonymous individual donor. The site was dedicated as the Willis Linn Jepson Prairie Preserve in a ceremony held on the Preserve on April 17, 1982. A cooperative use agreement with the University of California brought the Preserve into the University's Natural Reserve System in 1983. In 1987 the Preserve received additional recognition when the National Park Service named it a National Natural Landmark, a designation given to well preserved sites which illustrate a particular type of natural feature and provide high quality habitat for threatened and endangered species. In 1997 TNC transferred title of Jepson Prairie Preserve to the Solano Land Trust, a non-profit land trust dedicated to the protection and preservation of farmland and open space in Solano County. TNC retains a conservation easement over the Preserve that requires it to be conserved in perpetuity for native species and natural diversity.

Eucalyptus Trees

The few Australian blue gums–eucalyptus trees–that remain near the parking area are remnants of a much larger planting in and around Jepson Prairie. In 1910 a New York State lumber company bought 522 acres mostly north and east of Olcott Lake for $10.00, or $.02 per acre. They planned to plant blue gum seedlings and then subdivide and sell the land as managed furniture-grade timber plantation for $250 per acre. As many as 700,000 trees were planted, and a number of parcels sold. Soon thereafter the state forester declared that blue gum was suitable only for firewood. The project failed and most of the land was sold for delinquent taxes.

Blue gum is a very shallow-rooted tree, and it survived at Jepson Prairie only on the deepest soils. Surviving trees were cut for firewood during the Depression. Resprouts formed several groves when the land became a preserve. Because the eucalyptus are not native and added chemicals to the soil around them that inhibited native plants and encouraged weeds such as thistle, they have all been removed except for the few saved for shade and as a historic reminder.

This photo, taken just off the Preserve, shows many of the human impacts to the Jepson Prairie ecoregion, including remnant eucalyptus groves, power transmission lines, and roads.

– Current Management of Jepson Prairie

Jepson Prairie Preserve is managed by Solano Land Trust in close cooperation with the University of Californa Nature Reserve System, The Nature Conservancy and a committee of interested groups and individuals. There is a management plan for the Preserve which sets both short and long term objectives. The primary goal of the management plan is to maintain the native species and their habitats.

To maintain biodiversity, non-native plants and invasive weeds require active vegetation managemant. Without management they would outcompete native plants for limited resources such as water, soil and light. Vegetation management tools include grazing, prescribed burning and manual and chemical weed control. All of these are or have been employed at Jepson Prairie. To better understand the effectiveness of these management tools, several research and monitoring projects are being conducted at Jepson Prairie (see page 32).

Sheep grazing around an exclosure used in a research project to quantify the impacts and benefits of sheep grazing on the native and non-native plants at Jepson Prairie.

Monitoring is a large part of management research. This project, started in 1989, is conducted entirely by volunteers and annually monitors the population of the extremely rare Colusa Grass (see page 29).

Prescribed burning is an excellent vegetation management tool. It is particularly useful in controlling Medusahead (see page 59). However, it is very difficult to get a prescribed burn approved. This was a 2007 wildfire.

The Landscape

A first look out over the flat expanse of Jepson Prairie may seem to show little variety, but exploration reveals three distinct habitats: vernal pools, grasslands, and a marsh-riparian zone which is part of the Sacramento-San Joaquin Delta system. See page 17 for a general habitat map.

– Vernal Pools

A vernal pool is a temporary body of water. Vernal pools form when an impermeable layer at or near the surface of the landscape of low mounds and depressions traps winter rain to create shallow pools. These pools, if small, may dry between winter storms and then refill. Larger pools retain water all winter, critical to many of the aquatic species that must complete their life cycle in one wet season. All the pools will dry completely by summer. The next generation of plants and animals, as seeds and cysts (see page 63), awaits the next rainy season.

Vernal pools at Jepson Prairie filled with rainwater from a recent storm.

Climate plays an important role in what Californians call a vernal pool. While many places in the world have temporary rain puddles, the mass displays of vernal pool flowers only occur where there are mild wet winters followed by hot dry summers. This climate pattern is called a Mediterranean climate. The combination of water-trapping soil and a Mediterranean climate is unique to California and a handful of other places. These special conditions have allowed many species of plants and animals to evolve and adapt to living only in California vernal pools. Preservation of the vernal pool habitat is essential to the survival of these species.

At Jepson Prairie, the soils have a clay layer which expands when wet, creating Northern Claypan vernal pools. The soil at Jepson Prairie is derived from sedimentary rocks, mostly sandstone, which washed out from an alluvial fan from the Vaca Mountains to the west. The soils were deposited 60 to 100 thousand years ago. Over time rain trickled down through the soil, dissolving salts and nutrients and physically moved clay-sized particles downward. Today there is a clay-rich layer in the soil a foot or two below the surface. It also forms the bottom of Olcott Lake. Once these clays are saturated with water, they swell and form an impermeable layer. More rain just ponds on the surface of the soil. The result is large and small vernal pools.

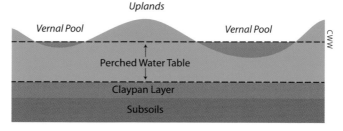

Cross section diagram showing a perched water table above the claypan layer.

Uplands

Vernal Pool *Vernal Pool*

Perched Water Table

Claypan Layer

Subsoils

The claypan layer is a major influence on the plant communities of the Preserve. It prevents leaching of salt and other alkaline compounds from the soils. Plants which grow in these soils must be relatively alkali and salt tolerant and shallow-rooted.

The pooling of water above the impermeable layer is the essential element in the vernal pool landscape, responsible for the distinctive flora and fauna. However, water also moves within the Preserve. In heavy rain years, water accumulated above the clay layer flows by gravity through the soil in a southeasterly direction, toward the central and very large pool—Olcott Lake—the lowest point in the Preserve, and toward Calhoun Cut, the tidal creek at the southern boundary. Water can rise in Olcott Lake to cover the road; it will then flow overland on the eastern part of the property to Calhoun Cut and the Delta water system. Small fish have been known to swim against this flow into Olcott, but they do not survive its drying in summer.

The chemistry of the trapped water changes throughout the season. In spring warming temperatures and longer days with increased sunlight and decreasing rain promote evaporation. In winter when the pool is full, Olcott's water tests very close to pure rainwater. By April the remaining water is significantly more alkaline, and its oxygen level drops.

Pools overflowing to the Delta.

– Playa Pools

Olcott Lake and several other very large vernal pools at Jepson Prairie are often called playa pools, or shallow alkaline lakes. They develop in low depressions on Pescadero Clay, a very heavy and saline clay. Most of the plants that occur in these larger pools are known for their salt tolerance. Among them are Alkali Heath, Alkali Mallow (page 37), Cressa and Saltgrass (page 59). While the playa pools may have rings of annual flowers on their margins in the spring, their appearance in the summer is very different from the smaller vernal pools at Jepson Prairie. Olcott Lake also contains two very rare playa pool endemic plants: Colusa Grass and Solano Grass (page 29). Also see page 28 for an account and photos of the playa pools during the dry season.

– Grasslands

Most great central valley vernal pools, including those at Jepson Prairie, occur in annual grassland, which is the most extensive habitat at the Preserve. The pastures we see today bear little resemblance to the same lands before settlement by Europeans and Americans. Researchers continue to try to determine what the "pristine" California grasslands looked like, and opinions are subject to revision (see page 13). We do know, unquestionably, that there has been massive change as non-native European annual forage grasses were introduced along with livestock starting in the eighteenth century and greatly accelerating in the nineteenth. These grasses, such as barleys, oats and bromes, evolved in another Mediterranean climate and were well adapted to flourish here. The non-native annuals have taken over; scientists refer to this as "conversion." At Jepson Prairie we also observe that most of the non-grass weeds cluster on the tops of the mounds, in the driest soils.

At first glance the grasslands may seem boring in their uniformity, but they serve vital functions in providing habitat for a number of vernal pool species. California Tiger Salamanders spend 90% of their life cycle in burrows in the upland, going to Olcott Lake to reproduce only once or twice during their lifetimes. And tiny bees essential to pollination of a number of vernal pool flowers depend on the uplands for their nests (see page 25). Many native grassland plants that were once much more common also persist, if in smaller numbers, in today's grasslands.

The grasslands are home to the native mammals of the Preserve, most of which are nocturnal rodents. Observing them means searching for signs of their presence, such as tracks, droppings, nests, burrows, and runways. The most abundant mammal at the Preserve is Botta's Pocket Gopher. Holes and piles of loose dirt, especially on the mounds, are frequently encountered signs of this species (see page 74). Visitors are most likely to see the Black-tailed Jackrabbit bounding through the grass. An early morning visitor may encounter a Striped Skunk, and Raccoon tracks have been spotted in the mud near Barker Slough and Calhoun Cut.

Grasslands at Jepson Prairie showing bunch-grasses and wild-flowers mixed in with the annual European grasses. Bunchgrasses are not common in the valley.

GK

Jepson Prairie's grasslands continue to be grazed by sheep, a use that has been documented back to the 1850s. Grazing is now a management tool, used under a formula designed to protect the rare and native plants and to reduce the buildup of thatch–dead annual grass that smothers germinating native plants. Recently published scientific studies show that removal of grazing from a vernal pool area had a significant negative effect on both vernal pools and their surrounding grasslands. Weeds and other non-native plants increased and native plants decreased. Even the aquatic organisms seemed to suffer a decline in abundance. The studies show that grazing animals are necessary to control the accumulation of thatch that originates from the non-native annual grasses, which would eventually choke out many of the native species.

Pristine Landscape Reconsidered

The appearance and plant composition of the great central valley, before European livestock and Mediterranean annual grasses took over in the 19th century, has been a subject of research and controversy. Early Spanish explorers did not make detailed records of the plants they found, but they changed the vegetation profoundly and irrevocably. The introduction of European livestock and grazing methods resulted in non-native annual grasses dominating the 13 million acres of California valley grassland.

For many years researchers based their ideas about the valley before it changed on plant surveys which began in the mid-19th century, as well as prevailing ecological theories developed in the eastern U.S., with its very different climate and vegetation. This led to the concept that the valley had been dominated by dense but not continuous perennial bunchgrasses, with annual flowering plants blooming abundantly in spring. Jepson Prairie was cited as an unusually good example of relict historic grassland as evidence for this concept.

More recently, botanists examining newly translated journals and other records from the Spanish expeditions have argued that they provide more information than previously acknowledged. The journals report great fields of colorful spring flowering plants suitable for grazing which rapidly and completely dried in summer. Recent studies also point out the problems associated with depending on reports and collections made after the proliferation of non-native grasses as evidence for reconstructing earlier landscapes. Jepson Prairie's needlegrass, more abundant than most great central valley locations, is believed to occur here because cooler, moist marine air from San Francisco Bay reaches the Preserve periodically throughout the hot summer months.

Currently, the best picture of the historic great central valley grassland in spring seems to be one described by John Muir. He said, "Here it is not as in our great western prairie, flowers sprinkled in grass, but grass in the flowers."

At Jepson Prairie, and on many other vernal pool landscapes, the grasslands, mima mounds, and vernal pools intermix in a mosaic of patterns. In the vernal pool landscape, the uplands and mima mounds are called the matrix, while the vernal pools are often referred to as the wetlands.

– Mima Mounds

Mima mounds, the fairly regularly spaced hillocks that rise less than two feet above the level of the swales in the grasslands of Jepson Prairie, are the subject of much visitor curiosity—as well as speculation and scientific investigation. Fields of low mounds like those at Jepson Prairie occur from northern Alaska to northern Mexico in western North America; other mound-patterned land is found in the Midwest, China, Africa and Australia. Geologists and geographers refer to this formation as mound microrelief.

Mima mounds are found only in grassy, treeless regions and are usually associated with some kind of impermeable soil layer. California mounds are usually 1 to 6 feet high and 9 to 60 feet in diameter. In a given area the mounds tend to be of uniform size and shape. They are hexagonal, circular or slightly oval on level ground. Mound material is usually loose and unstratified and has a high proportion of silt.

The origin of mounds has been debated since the mid-19th century; more than two dozen theories have been proposed. The most persistent theories attribute them to: periglacial conditions, localized deposition, formation by gophers, and seismicity.

Periglacial origin: The regularity of mound areas resembles "arctic-patterned ground," formed by ice age cracking or heaving. However the internal structure of the mounds at Jepson Prairie differs from most cold-region mounds, and the great central valley was not overly influenced by the last ice age.

Localized deposition: Perhaps clumps of grass on slightly higher ground could trap windblown soil and debris, while the surrounding ground level was lowered by rain-wash or wind erosion. This doesn't account for coarse sediment found in some mounds, but it would explain the high proportion of silt.

Formation by gophers: This popular theory suggests that burrowing rodents formed the mounds over eons by using the higher, drier areas as nesting sites and digging foraging tunnels in those areas. Their activity loosened and raised the soil. Without question many mounds provide homes for gophers. Most evidence suggests that the animals prefer to occupy the mounds' well-drained soils. Recent research at the University of California, Berkeley, seems to show that gopher activity, if it did not form the mounds, now maintains them.

Seismicity: Loose particles on a smooth surface will clump into small piles when vibrated repeatedly–think about dirt in the back of a pickup truck. By analogy, the soil at Jepson gathered into mounds as a result of the many earthquakes that have occurred in the last 10,000 years.

Perhaps there was a combination of causes: A substrate was formed by glacial outwash or alluvial deposits (or volcanic activity in some areas) and subsequently developed into a hardpan or claypan. Additional sediment was deposited by streams, forming the upper soils. During episodes of drying or freezing, networks of deep cracks developed in the soils. Higher and drier areas permitted the growth of denser vegetation. Burrowing animals may have contributed to greater microrelief by their burrowing activity. The grasses tended to trap and hold sediment, while surrounding barer ground was subject to erosion by rain and wind. Together these forces increased mound height by raising the center and wearing down the edges.

Despite the mystery about their origin, Jepson's mima mounds have very different vegetation from the vernal pools and swales surrounding them. Their upper soils do not saturate during the wet season and have been almost totally invaded by non-native annual grasses and forbs.

Mima mounds and a ponded vernal pool can be seen in the foreground. The wind turbines are south of Jepson Prairie Preserve. Continued expansion of wind energy harvesting may threaten unprotected vernal pool grasslands.

15

– Marsh & Riparian

Jepson Prairie is located immediately west of the vast marshlands of the Sacramento-San Joaquin Delta. Small fingers of those marshlands come westward into the Preserve along Barker Slough, crossed by Cook Road near the north boundary, and Calhoun Cut, which runs along the southern border of the Preserve and is crossed by Highway 113 at the southeastern corner. Both waterways are influenced by tidal action and by seasonal variability of water. Year-round water availability supports summer vegetation; the marsh is green when the remainder of the Preserve is brown and dry. Rushes, bulrush and tules occur in succession as one proceeds closer to the channel and follows it toward the Delta.

The grassland at Jepson Prairie is notable for its lack of woody vegetation, such as shrubs and trees, with the exception of the non-native eucalyptus (see page 8). Low-growing willows and similar riparian species, however, do occur along Calhoun Cut. Restoration plantings of willows along Barker Slough in the early 1990s have persisted and have attracted beavers.

BW

Willows and emergent marsh along edge of a beaver pond in Barker Slough. This was a restoration planting that has thrived and attracted wildlife.

A pair of River Otters (*Lontra canadensis*) in Calhoun Cut. Part of the old Lindsey Slough, Calhoun Cut was deepened and straightened during the land boom in the early 1900s.

DW

Soils & Habitats of Jepson Prairie Preserve

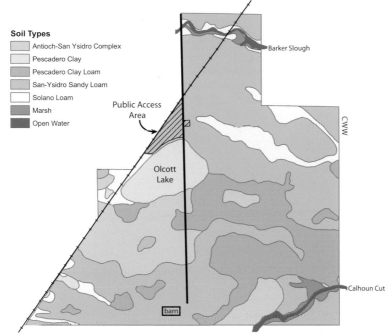

Soil Types
- Antioch-San Ysidro Complex
- Pescadero Clay
- Pescadero Clay Loam
- San-Ysidro Sandy Loam
- Solano Loam
- Marsh
- Open Water

Barker Slough

Public Access Area

Olcott Lake

CWW

Calhoun Cut

barn

— Soils & Plant Communities

Soil composition and structure drive the hydrology and plant communities. Depth to claypan and surface topography determine whether water ponds on the surface. Whether or not water ponds determines if the plant community is dominated by vernal pool or grassland species.

Antioch-San Ysidro Complex: These soils have abundant micro-relief. They are often characterized by large complexes of swales and pools interspersed with large mima mound. Areas within these soils provide some of the most diverse plant displays on Jepson Prairie.

Pescadero Clay: The claypan in Pescadero Clay is often at the soil surface, and playa pools have developed here (see page 28).

Pescadero Clay Loam: These soils support small playa pools and low mound and swale micro-relief. The micro-relief is more subtle than in the Antioch-San Ysidro Complex, and the soils are more alkaline.

San Ysidro Sandy Loam: These areas are of relatively deep and well-drained soils. They support mostly grassland vegetation with occasional small vernal pools and low mima mounds.

Solano Loam: This soil is basically flat and occurs in low lying areas. Water does not usually pond more than an inch, but the soils are often saturated. In early spring these soils may appear to be "yellow brick roads" of Yellow Carpet (page 39) and other vernal pool plants.

Aquatic Phase

The aquatic phase of the annual vernal pool "life cycle" begins shortly after the first fall rains. At Jepson Prairie the clay soils expand rapidly and become impermeable to water percolating downward. Once the soils are saturated, additional rainfall perches above the clay and the pools begin to fill. The aquatic phase lasts until the winter rainstorms have passed and warmer spring weather sets in. Small pools may dry between storms, while the larger pools and playas will remain ponded until late spring or early summer.

Jepson Prairie vernal pools during the peak of the aquatic phase. At this point, water is flowing across the landscape toward the Delta (see map on page 5).

DW

To many people, the aquatic phase of a vernal pool may resemble a mud puddle, but to the many organisms that depend on vernal pools (see pages 60-65), it represents much more. The animals that can be found in and around vernal pools are of three general types—those that only live in vernal pools, those that use vernal pools for part of their life cycle, and those that visit vernal pools to feed or rest. Of these groups, the animals that can only live in vernal pools are unique and striking. Many of these species are also threatened by extinction due to past and ongoing destruction of vernal pool habitat.

While most of the aquatic organisms that are endemic to vernal pools are microscopic, several larger freshwater crustaceans—fairy shrimp, clam shrimp and tadpole shrimp—can be observed swimming and feeding. These freshwater crustaceans have evolved a very unusual adaption to survive the extreme conditions of summer drought—they produce cysts (see page 63).

The animals that occupy vernal pools for only part of their life cycle consist of two general categories—amphibians and insects. Both of these groups use vernal pools during their larval stage.

Amphibians mate and lay eggs in vernal pools. Their larvae are aquatic until they metamorphose into their terrestrial form. Then they live out of the water until the urge to reproduce brings them back to the vernal

Seasonal Changes

Conservancy Fairy Shrimp (*Branchinecta conservatio*) are endangered. They are translucent and grow to an inch or more (see page 61).

Vernal Pool Tadpole Shrimp (*Lepidurus packardi*) are also endangered. They can grow to the size of a silver dollar (see page 62).

pools. During late spring, you can see many young frogs, newly metamorphosed, on the edges of the vernal pools. At Jepson Prairie, only two amphibians occur–California Tiger Salamander (see page 20) and Pacific Chorus Frogs (see page 66).

Some insects follow the same type of life cycle. They breed, usually on the wing, and then deposit their eggs in vernal pools. Their aquatic larvae are fierce predators and grow quickly due to the abundance of prey in the vernal pool aquatic ecosystem. Eventually they undergo metamorphosis and emerge as terrestrial adults able to fly off to new habitats. Some insects are great swimmers even in their adult stage (see page 60).

Those simply visiting the vernal pools during the aquatic phase consist mostly of migrating waterfowl and shorebirds (see pages 69-72). They come to feast on the abundant aquatic organisms. As the aquatic phase progresses into the flowering phase, the visitors also change. Early in the season, the pools are visited by ducks and geese which feed on crustaceans and submerged plants. As the pools begin to dry, egrets and herons come to feed on small frogs, snails and insects. Then there are the other animals that come to prey on the birds in a complex food web.

A Great Egret visits during the last of the aquatic phase to prey on tadpoles, California Tiger Salamander larve and insect larvae.

– California Tiger Salamanders

California Tiger Salamanders (*Ambystoma californiense*) are an endangered species that is endemic to California. The reason they are endangered is over 55% of their original habitat was destroyed when the great central valley was converted to agricultural and urban uses in the late 1800s. They now persist mostly on the margins of the valley, in the foothills of the Sierra Nevada, and in the inner Coast Ranges on lands used for sheep and cattle grazing.

Jepson Prairie is typical of the majority of this range in that it receives an average of only 18 inches of rain per year. Almost all of this rain falls in the winter. From late May to mid-October, rainfall here averages 0.4 inches. Because of this long dry season, only two amphibian species are able to persist at Jepson Prairie–California Tiger Salamander (CTS) and Pacific Chorus Frogs (see page 66).

Adult California Tiger Salamander (*aka* CTS).

AC

In order to cope with California's hot, dry summers, CTS spend the vast majority of their lives underground in rodent burrows. In fact, the average California Tiger Salamander spends over 95% of its post-metamorphic life underground. Over most of their range, CTS depend on the burrows of California Ground Squirrels (*Otospermophilus beecheyi*), but at Jepson Prairie the salamanders use burrows made by Botta's Pocket Gophers (see page 75). Even in the middle of the summer, the burrows remain relatively cool and moist.

After entering the burrow system, CTS leave their underground habitat only on rainy winter nights. Yearly activity begins as soon as the first rains fall in late October. At this time, first year juveniles search for better burrows, since the previous summer when they emerged from the playa pool, they were forced to enter one of the first burrows they could find in order to escape the hot, dry weather.

Next to emerge are the adult males, which make their way down to the playa pools in order to await the adult females. Once the females arrive breeding occurs, and the females attach their eggs to pieces of vegetation or to the bottom of the pond. The adults then migrate back to the burrow system and make sure to get underground before the end of February so that even during a dry spring they will be underground before the rains end for the year.

CTS egg with seed shrimp (see page 63) in the foreground. You can see the developing CTS in the egg sack.

CTS larva nearing the metamorph stage. It has developed legs and lungs and is resorbing its external gills.

Metamorph CTS entering a burrow. They must get underground quickly to avoid dessication in the late spring heat.

Adult CTS.

The eggs that were left in the pool hatch after 2-4 weeks. The larval salamanders that emerge from these eggs are fully aquatic with external gills and a large dorsal fin. During the larval period, which lasts 3-5 months, the salamanders grow very rapidly, doubling in size approximately every two weeks. The reason they can grow so quickly is that the playa pools are an amazing source of food, with very high concentrations of small crustaceans on which to feed.

As the pools begin to dry up in the spring, the salamanders metamorphose into their terrestrial form by resorbing their gills and fin. They must finish their metamorphosis before the ponds dry up, or they will be stranded on the dry pool bed and die. In a very dry year, 100% of the larvae may die in this manner. Those larvae that do finish metamorphosis emerge from the pool at night and immediately seek a burrow. At this time of year, late May or June, it may not have rained for over two months and daytime temperatures may reach 105°F.

If the salamanders are not underground within a couple hours of sunrise, they will desiccate on the surface. Once underground, the average salamander takes four years to reach adult size, at which time it can return to the playa pool to breed. If they manage to escape predation and desiccation during their annual migrations, CTS can live to be up to 13 years old.

This long lifespan is important for the salamanders' persistence, because California experiences both intra-annual and inter-annual variation in rainfall. CTS deal with intra-annual variation by being underground during the hot and dry portion of the year. But what if inter-annual variation leads to a number of dry years in a row? This could lead to complete larval mortality over several years. The CTS's long life allows it to survive a series of dry years and still be around to breed when another wet year arrives.

Flowering Phase

The flowering phase at Jepson Prairie begins earlier than in most vernal pool landscapes. It also overlaps with the end of the aquatic phase. Flowers begin blooming in the grasslands and on the edges of the vernal pools in early to mid-March. The flowering phase continues until all of the pools and playas have completely dried.

Vernal pools at Jepson Prairie during the early flowering phase. See pages 34-59 for a photo guide to the common plants.

CWW

Over 200 species of plants grow in California vernal pools. Of those, half are entirely endemic to this unique habitat. Plants that grow in vernal pools have several unique adaptations that allow them to survive the extremes of flood and drought. Most vernal pool plants are annuals, living only during the short winter and spring seasons before setting seed and dying. These plants tend to be of small stature, but with relatively large flowers. Their goal is not to grow big and survive a long time, but to reproduce and make plenty of seeds for future generations.

Having few leaves and very showy flowers is part of the vernal pool plants' strategy for producing abundant seed. The concentric circles, ribbons and patches of pink, yellow, white and blue blossoms effectively attract their pollinators. While many different types of insects visit vernal pool flowers, some have evolved to depend on only one or a few types of flowers. See page 24 for more information on the specialist bees that feed their offspring on the pollen of vernal pool flowers.

Another unusual survival adaptation of vernal pool plants is their strategy for seed dispersal. Most don't even try to disperse their seeds. Having evolved to live in a flooded area for most of their life, and requiring a drying down phase to stimulate flowering and seed produc-tion—why would they want to cast their seeds into unsuitable habitat? A number of vernal pool species literally plant their seeds at the base of the parent plant. This ensures that the seeds are in the best possible location to germinate, grow and reproduce the following year.

Being an annual plant with dedicated pollinators and setting seed quickly are good ways to deal with the short spring and long drought phases of this habitat. Vernal pool plants have also had to develop other adapta-tions to deal with the aquatic phase. Most plants would drown if flooded

Coyote-thistle during the aquatic phase.

Coyote-thistle in the early flowering phase.

Coyote-thistle in the late flowering phase.

for long periods. Vernal pool plants deal with this in several unique ways. Some pipe air to their roots through long, hollow stems or leaves. Others absorb atmospheric gasses (air) directly from the water.

Coyote-thistle is one of the vernal pool endemic plants that has evolved a unique way to pipe air to its roots. During the aquatic phase, the plant produces hollow, cylindrical leaves that stick up out of the water. Air gets to the plant's roots through this tube. Later, as the pools dry, these leaves become solid, leafier and spiny. The photos above show the amazing physical changes that Coyote-thistles go through each year.

Other vernal pool plants bring air to their roots by producing floating leaves. The leaves can absorb enough air for the entire plant. This adaptation also has the advantage of shading out other plants, thereby reducing competition. Annual Semaphoregrass, shown at right and on page 56, is one of the plants that employs this strategy for surviving the aquatic phase.

Annual Semaphore-grass (see page 56) uses floating leaves to absorb air to transport to its roots. The floating leaves also shade out other plants that might compete with it.

Many vernal pool plants spend the aquatic phase entirely under water. They survive by absorbing dissolved gasses directly from the water. But because warm water has less dissolved gasses than cold water, they absorb air from the water at night. Several groups of plants, including many desert species, absorb air at night instead of during the day, but only vernal pool plants do it under water.

Because vernal pool plants are native to their environment, they have had tens of thousands of years to adapt to the extreme conditions of living in a vernal pool. Most non-native plant species cannot survive in a vernal pool.

Playa pools: The preceeding discussion of the vernal pool plants applies mostly to the smaller, clear water pools and not the the large, turbid playa pools. More on the unique plants of the playa pools may be found in the drought phase sections (see pages 27-29).

– Native Specialist Pollinators

Vernal pools are noted for their multi-colored rings and ribbons of native flowers. Each species occupies a different topographic position and micro-habitat within the pool. And each produces an abundant and dense display of flowers which all bloom at the same time.

Display of abundant wildflowers that bloom in the vernal pools of Jepson Prairie.

MEH

Besides delighting the eye of human visitors, there is an important ecological reason for the flowers of a given species to bloom in mass synchrony. Many of the showiest vernal pool flowers (Yellow Carpet, Meadowfoam, Goldfields, and Downingia) are pollinated by native specialist bees in the family Andrenidae. These solitary, ground-nesting bees use the pollen of specific flowers to feed their young. And, during the course of collecting pollen to provision their nests, they perform the vital function of cross-pollinating the vernal pool flowers.

A female solitary, pollen specialist bee (*Andrena [Hesperandrena] baeriae*) **collecting pollen from goldfields. For more information on specialist pollinators visit** **www.vernalpools.org/Thorp.**

This and most subsequent native pollinator photos, unless otherwise annotated, by Dennis Briggs and courtesy of Robbin W. Thorp.

Each of the four plant groups listed above has one or more native specialist bees that collects pollen only from them. Female bees that collect pollen from one or a few closely related flowers are called oligolectic (from oligo = few, legene = to gather). They require pollen from the flowers to provide protein for the development of their offspring. The life cycle of these bees is closely synchronized with that of their pollen host flowers.

While generalist and non-native bees, such as the honey bee, and other insects also visit most of these flowers and may potentially pollinate them, research shows that at least some of these flowers may require their specialist pollinators for successful reproduction and seed set.

A female specialist bee, *Andrena blennospermatis*, collecting pollen from Yellow Carpet (see page 39).

A female specialist bee, *Panurginus* "new species", collecting pollen from Horned Downingia (see page 51).

A female specialist bee, *Andrena (Hesperandrena) pulverea*, collecting pollen from Meadow-foam (see page 37).

– Life Cycle of Native Specialist Bees

Female bees in the family Andrenidae, which specialize on pollen of vernal pool flowers, are on the wing only in early spring when their host plants are in flower. The life cycle of the bee is closely tuned to that of its host plant's bloom period. The bees emerge at or just before their host flowers start to bloom. Male bees emerge shortly before the females. Mating occurs as soon as females emerge. Females begin constructing their brood nests immediately after mating.

This open tumulus indicates that the female bee is out foraging for pollen and/or nectar.

The female bees construct their nests in the soil of the upland areas surrounding vernal pools. The presence of such bee nests is revealed by ant-mound-like clumps of excavated soil (tumuli) at the surface of the soil. A closed tumulus indicates the female is in her burrow constructing it. An open tumulus indicates the female bee is afield foraging for pollen and/or nectar as provisions for her offspring.

The basic nest architecture consists of a vertical shaft penetrating the soil for a few inches before becoming a lateral tunnel ending in a single brood chamber. A newly constructed brood chamber has a polished look because of its waterproof lining. This waxy lining is secreted by the

A completed brood cell showing its shiny, water-proof lining. The female bee uses body secretions to create this waterproofing.

Early stages of provisioning the brood chamber with pollen and nectar.

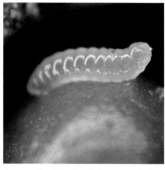

A newly hatched larva of the specialist bee on its food ball, a combination of pollen and nectar from the specific plant it requires for nutrition.

Fully developed larva that will transform into an adult bee in the fall. That bee will remain underground until its host flowers bloom again the next spring.

female and painted over the inner surface of the brood cell.

When brood chamber construction is complete, the female bee forages for pollen on her preferred host flowers. She grooms pollen from her body and packs it into specialized brushes of hair on her hind legs for transport back to her nest.

As the dry pollen food provisions accumulate in the brood cell, the female adds nectar, moistening the mass to a dough-like consistency. When the pollen ball is complete, she lays a single egg on top. She then constructs a plug closing off the entrance to the chamber with spirally-arranged soil particles. After closing off the brood chamber the mother bee has no further contact with her offspring.

The female will then begin another lateral shaft to a new brood chamber. The lateral shafts are arranged at the bottom of the vertical shaft much like spokes of a wheel. During the brief flowering period, a female may provision up to 30 eggs, and many fewer in a dry year. Most of her effort goes into providing a secure haven and sufficient food for only a very few offspring.

After a few weeks, the egg hatches and the larva begins feeding on the pollen and nectar provisions. After consuming all of the pollen ball in the spring, the larva rests in its chamber for the remainder of the summer. In the fall, the larva pupates and transforms into an adult. The adult sits in the brood chamber until the following spring when it emerges to continue its life cycle in association with the flowering of its pollen host plant.

The majority of the life cycle of these bees is spent in the brood cell. Overwintering as an adult is an adaptation to synchronize the bees with the early spring bloom of their pollen host plants. During droughts, the adults may remain underground for more than a year or two.

Drought Phase

During the hot, dry summer months, vernal pools lie brown and barren. The drought phase begins as the last of the water evaporates and the soil begins to dry out. The aquatic organisms have been gone for a month or more, but have deposited their cysts (page 63) to ensure the next generation. By now the grasslands are brown and dormant until the rains return in the fall. Most of the vernal pool plants have also set seed and have withered and died. The drought phase can last for six to eight months.

The drought phase is absolutely necessary for the plants and animals that are entirely dependent upon vernal pools. Without the drought phase, the cysts and seeds could not produce a new generation next year. They need to bake under the summer sun before they can be triggered into hatching or germinating when the rains return in the fall and winter.

The animals that use vernal pools for only part of their life cycle have moved on. California Tiger Salamanders (page 20) and Pacific Chorus Frogs are spending the drought phase underground. The insects that use vernal pools in their aquatic larval form have moved onto other water sources.

But even in the heat of the summer, the vernal pool landscape is far from dead. Some of the vernal pool plants wait until the heat of summer to bloom and set seed (page 28). Insects, birds and mammals continue to visit the vernal pool grasslands. They come to feed on the seeds left behind. When they do, other animals come to feed upon them. Thus vernal pools form a large and very complex food chain critical to the survival of many species.

The drought phase is an excellent time to visit the nearby marshes and sloughs (page 16). Because of the permanent water, these areas remain green through much of the summer. Their riparian vegetation also provides shade and perches. These areas are an oasis for insects, birds and mammals that concentrate here during the drought phase.

CWW

Grasslands of Jepson Prairie during the summer drought phase.

– Olcott Lake

The word playa is Spanish for beach. The term playa pool is often used to describe shallow, alkaline lakes that dry up during the summer. The dried surface of many of the pools can resemble a beach, primarily due to the very sparse vegetation and whitish, alkaline soils. Olcott Lake is usually called a playa pool to distinguish it from the smaller vernal pools interspersed in the grassland. Playa pools are also different from vernal pools in other ways. While they do support some of the typical annual vernal pool plants, particularly along their margins, a large proportion of their flora is summer-blooming, perennial halophytes (from halo = salt, phyte = loving). Olcott remains relatively green during at least the first half of the drought phase.

Olcott Lake photographed in August. The perennial species here do not bloom until the summer. Notice the whitish, alkaline soil between the plants.

Alkali Heath and Cressa (below) are common plants in Olcott Lake which do not occur in the shallower and less alkaline pools in the surrounding grassland. They bloom during the heat of the summer. Other species that occur in Olcott Lake, but generally not in the smaller pools, include Alkali Mallow (page 37), Cupped Downingia (page 51), and the rare grasses, Solano Grass (*Tuctoria mucronata*) and Colusa Grass (*Neostapfia colusana*), discussed on the next page.

Alkali Heath (*Frankenia salina*) **exudes salty water.**

Cressa (*Cressa truxillensis*) **being visited by a sweat bee.**

Colusa Grass (*Neostapfia colusana*) is endemic to playa pools. It is listed under the state and federal Endangered Species Acts. The population in Olcott Lake is relatively large and stable. Volunteers have been monitoring this population every summer since 1989. (Also see page 59.)

– Playa Pool Endemic Grasses

An entire tribe of grasses—the Orcuttieae—is endemic to playa pools or shallow vernal lakes. There are eight species in three closely related genera. They range from playas in Baja California up through the great central valley and into the Modoc Plateau. Each of the species is extremely rare, and all are listed as threatened or endangered.

These grasses have a unique quality not seen in other grasses. They produce an exudate or secretion that is sticky, acidic and very foul tasting. This probably deters animals from eating the plants.

Olcott Lake is home to two of these rare grasses—Colusa Grass and Solano Grass. However, the Solano Grass has not been seen since 1993 and may be extirpated from the site.

Solano Grass (*Tuctoria mucronata*) is also listed under both the state and federal Endangered Species Acts. It is the rarest of the endemic playa pool grasses and is currently known from only three vernal pools: one a few miles away from Jepson Prairie and two others in Yolo County. The historic population at Olcott Lake has not been seen since 1993 and may have been the victim of over collecting. (Also see page 59.)

Rare, Threatened & Endangered Species

Many organisms are naturally rare due to limited distribution or low numbers. A rare animal or plant can become threatened or endangered, and be formally listed under the state and federal Endangered Species Acts, when human activities impinge upon the chances for its continued survival in the wild. Catastrophic natural events, such as fires and floods, can also endanger rare species.

Most often the primary threat to a species is habitat destruction, such as conversion to more intensive agriculture or urban development. In other situations the threat is due to direct mortality of the organism. In the case of Solano Grass (page 29), over-collection for scientific use may have played a role in its extirpation from Olcott Lake. In the case of California Tiger Salamanders (page 20), individuals can be killed when trying to cross a busy road, which frequently happens in Sonoma County.

Besides the species above and those mentioned elsewhere in this guide—fairy and tadpole shrimp (pages 19, 61, 62), Prairie Bells (page 34), Bogg's Lake Hedge-hyssop (page 36), Dwarf Downingia (pages 36, 51), Legenere (pages 36, 55), Baker's Navarretia (page 38), Solano Popcorn-flower (page 38), Alkali Milkvetch (page 49), Heckard's Peppergrass (page 54)–Jepson Prairie is home to another half dozen or more species which qualify as rare, threatened or endangered.

© Ken Davis 2010

Delta Green Ground Beetles (*Elaphrus viridis***) come in two patterns–spotted and solid. They are only known from about 11 square miles in and near Jepson Prairie Preserve.**

The Delta Green Ground Beetle is another endangered species, and is entirely endemic to Jepson Prairie and some nearby properties. These tiny beetles forage on the edges of Olcott Lake and nearby playas from January to May. They hunt for soft-bodied prey, such as Springtails (page 64), when the weather is warm and calm. They mate in February and March.

Little else is known about their life cycle, including why they come in two colors that are not sex-related. They are thought to aestivate during the summer and fall, but in what developmental phase (egg, larva, pupa or adult) is unknown.

Jepson Prairie's ability to support species that are rarely found elsewhere in California is the result of the lack of intensive disturbance and development that has negatively impacted many areas of the great central valley. The fact that the Preserve is also surrounded by signifi-cant areas of natural habitat also helps buffer the Preserve from potential indirect effects resulting from incompatible adjacent land uses.

Conservation & Stewardship

Conservation can be defined as the act of preserving, guarding or protecting. As a verb, conserve usually means saving something for a later use. You can conserve energy, land, or other resources. Often to save something simply means not to use it or to put it away. But, groceries just placed on a shelf can spoil if not given the proper conditions.

Stewardship is the act of caring for or improving over time. To steward something along requires active involvement in its wellbeing. Stewardship is a dynamic and evolving process of looking after the health of something valuable. Using the grocery analogy, vegetables stay fresher in the refrigerator than on the counter top.

Real world conservation requires stewardship in order to nurture the plants and animals we are trying to conserve, and to fight against invasive weeds and other threats to their welfare. Both conservation and stewardship can take many forms and involve unlikely partnerships. At Jepson Prairie Preserve, many stakeholder groups and individuals work together to promote conservation and stewardship.

– Land Protection

As stated in earlier sections, the Jepson Prairie Preserve is under a conservation easement that prohibits activities that would alter its ability to support the unique animals, plants and their habitats. Basically, land protection prohibits conversion to other uses that would prevent the species and habitats from surviving. Several additional parcels in the Greater Jepson Prairie Ecoregion are similarly protected.

– Active Management

Vegetation and invasive weed management are important components of land stewardship. Accumulation of plant biomass or thatch suppresses the more delicate native flowering plants. Invasive species can entirely displace native vegetation and usually have no local predators. Several approaches are being used to control non-native and invasive plants.

Sheep grazing is used to help control the non-native grasses and weeds at Jepson Prairie.

Grazing helps to reduce thatch build-up. Herbicides are proving effective for spot treatment of some invasive plants. As mentioned earlier, fire can be very effective to control some invasives such as Medusahead, but prescribed burns are difficult to plan, permit and execute.

– Ongoing Research

Research is critical to understanding the needs of individual species and general ecosystem response to management actions. Research and monitoring inform management decisions at Jepson Prairie, but are often applicable to similar landscapes or throughout the range of a species. Several research and monitoring projects at Jepson Prairie have been going on for a decade or more. These long term projects may provide insight into how species will respond to climate change.

California Tiger Salamander Research

Over the past 10 years, researchers from UC Davis have monitored the CTS population at Jepson Prairie using a large pitfall trap array that includes 745 traps and 2780 meters of fencing spread over 9 miles. The traps are checked at sunrise after every rainy night and also during a period of up to two months in the spring when the metamorphosed salamanders are emerging from the drying pools. This has resulted in the capture of 34,597 salamanders. Using these data, researchers have learned how far the salamanders migrate, which other factors affect their habitat preferences, and how climatic conditions regulate their populations. All of this information is used to help conserve this endangered species throughout its range.

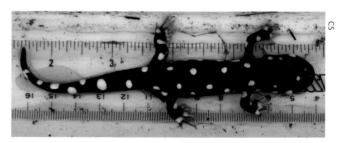

California Tiger Salamander (CTS) being measured as part of a decade long research project.

In addition to the CTS research highlighted above, current and recent research and monitoring projects include: long term native and non-native plant transect monitoring, long term monitoring of Colusa Grass (see page 9), pollination biology of Meadowfoam, study of microbes in nectar and relationships with pollinators, grazing exclusion studies (see page 9), studies of fire and grazing on native and non-native plants including perennial bunchgrasses, and studies of native specialist pollinators (see pages 24-26).

− Education & Outreach

One of the most important components of stewardship is outreach. People need to see and connect with organisms and their habitats before they can feel a passion to conserve them. Education programs provide opportunities for students and the public to see and learn about Jepson Prairie. Formal courses are offered through UC Davis and several nearby colleges and universities. The Jepson Prairie Docent Program (see inside back cover) gives public tours on weekends and offers tours to K-12 classes and other youth groups.

Public tours offered by the Jepson Prairie Docents are popular family events. Tours are held on Saturdays and Sundays from early March through Mother's Day. Special tours can be arranged.

− How You Can Help

The best way you can help Jepson Prairie and other vernal pools in California is to spread the word about how beautiful and fascinating they are. Bring your friends and family out for a guided tour. Photograph the plants and animals you encounter and give a talk to your home-owners' association or church group.

You can also join the Jepson Prairie Docents. They share their knowledge of the area with visitors to the Preserve. You don't need to be an expert, just an enthusiastic guide to the land-scape and habitats of the Preserve.

33

DW

Prairie Pointers, Shooting-star
FEB-MAR
2-8 INCHES

Dodecatheon clevelandii ssp. *patulum*
NATIVE

The flowers are usually white, but can be pink-tipped or even all pink. They point down when in flower and then point up as the seeds begin to mature. At Jepson Prairie they are most often found on the slopes of mima mounds.

CWW

Prairie Bells, Fragrant Fritillary
FEB-MAR
6-10 INCHES

Fritillaria liliacea
NATIVE/RARE

Prefers heavy soils in grasslands. At Jepson Prairie it is found on the slopes of mima mounds. In good years this beautiful and fragrant member of the lily family may reach 18 inches and have as many as 10 flowers.

CWW

Paper Onion
MAR-APR
8-12 INCHES

Allium amplectens
NATIVE

The flowers can be white to pink and are only 3/8 inch across. This is a bulb-producing native species closely related to onions and garlic. Both Native Americans and European settlers used the bulbs to flavor their cooking.

DW

Muilla
MAR-APR
6-10 INCHES

Muilla maritima
NATIVE

The flowers can be white to cream and are only 3/8 inch across. Members of this genus are similar to the wild onions (see above), but without the onion odor. The genus name is *Allium* spelled backward.

DW

White Hyacinth
APR-MAY
12-18 INCHES

Triteleia hyacinthina
NATIVE

White Hyacinth is a bulb-producing perennial grassland plant. Early in the season, the plants produce one or a few grass-like leaves. By the time the flowers are ready to bloom, the leaves have dried up.

DW

Fringed Water Plantain
Damasonium californicum

APR-MAY
3-15 INCHES
NATIVE

Fringed Water Plantain has very striking three-petaled flowers. Each petal is fringed around the edges. It occurs in a variety of wetland habitats in California. At Jepson Prairie it is found in some of the wetter pools.

CWW

Yarrow
Achillea millefolium

APR-MAY
12-18 INCHES
NATIVE

This white flowered Yarrow is the same species often cultivated in a variety of colors. It is native and prefers the tops of mima mounds. A tea made from the leaves has analgesic properties and was used by Native Americans.

DW

Blow Wives
Achyrachaena mollis

MAR-MAY
4-12 INCHES
NATIVE

Blow Wives are most commonly observed when in fruit as shown at left. What you see is the pappus at the top of each seed in the head. See page 40 for a photograph of the small and inconspicuous yellow flowers.

MEH

Miner's Lettuce
Claytonia perfoliata

FEB-MAR
2-8 INCHES
NATIVE

The flowers are usually white but can be pink. The most distinguishing characteristic is the cup-shaped leaf that completely surrounds the stem below the flowers. The foliage and flowers are edible as salad greens or pot herbs.

CWW

Mouse-ear Chickweed
Cerastium glomeratum

MAR-MAY
1-12 INCHES
INTRODUCED

Common weed of most habitats of California. Because of its small stature, it does not readily displace native species. At Jepson Prairie it prefers slightly mesic habitats such as the edges of vernal pools or swales.

35

CB

Sticky Sand-spurrey

APR-JUN
6-12 INCHES
NATIVE

Spergularia macrotheca ssp. *longistyla*

Flowers can be white to pale pink. This is one of the largest flowered of the sand-spurreys. It is also a native. It is entirely endemic to the great central valley and prefers alkaline soils and areas of low competition.

DW

Valley Tassels

MAR-APR
6-12 INCHES
NATIVE

Castilleja attenuata

This grassland species is also known as White-tipped Owl's-clover. The flowers are long tubes with three inflated sacks near the top which have a series of pink, yellow and black spots that resemble tiny faces.

DW

Bogg's-Lake Hedge-hyssop

MAR-MAY
1-6 INCHES
NATIVE/RARE

Gratiola heterosepala

This plant has tiny (¼ inch) flowers that usually bloom while the plant is still in very shallow standing water. The tubular flowers are white and yellow. They are self pollinating and often do not open entirely.

DW

Dwarf Downingia

APR-JUN
1-3 INCHES
NATIVE/RARE

Downingia pusilla

The flowers of this species are less than ¼ inch across. Unlike most of the other Downingia, this plant is not pollinated by specialist bees. There are both blue flowered and white flowered forms on Jepson Prairie (see page 51).

JG

Legenere

APR-MAY
3-12 INCHES
NATIVE/RARE

Legenere limosa

This vernal pool endemic plant prefers the deeper and wetter vernal pools. Legenere flowers can be of two types. The most common type is self-pollinating and does not have any petals (see page 55).

DW

Meadowfoam

Limnanthes douglasii ssp. *rosea*

MAR-MAY
4-8 INCHES
NATIVE

White with rose colored veins on the petals. Frequently found ringing the vernal pools. Seeds from the plants in this genus produce oils that are used in the cosmetic industry. Pollinated by specialist bees (see page 24).

JJB

Flax-flowered Linanthus

Linanthus liniflorus

MAY-JUN
4-10 INCHES
NATIVE

Blooms in open grassland after most of the grasses have set seed and turned brown. The white flowers are very showy and delicate. Another common name for this genus is Whisker Brush due to the very narrow leaves.

DW

Bindweed

Convolvulus arvensis

MAR-OCT
VINE
INVASIVE

Bindweed plants produce extensive and very deep (30 feet) root systems. It has been a serious weed in California for nearly a century. There are no known control techniques suitable for wild areas.

MEH

Stemless Morning Glory

Calystegia subacaulis

APR-MAY
4-8 INCHES
NATIVE

This is a native member of the bindweed family. The plant is annual and generally inconspicuous until it unfolds its 2-3 inch wide flowers. Uncommon in the grasslands of Jepson Prairie, but magnificent when found.

DW

Alkali Mallow

Malvella leprosa

JUN-JUL
4-8 INCHES
NATIVE

This is a native perennial member of the mallow family. On Jepson Prairie, it occurs almost exclusively in Olcott Lake where it blooms in the summer. For more information on summer blooming species (see page 28).

DW

Baker's Navarretia
Navarretia leucocephala ssp. *bakeri*

APR-MAY
1-4 INCHES
NATIVE/RARE

This vernal pool endemic is most often seen on the margins of Olcott Lake. In some years it can be quite abundant and showy. This rare subspecies generally occurs in the Coast Ranges and not in the great central valley.

CWW

Small Popcornflower
Plagiobothrys humistratus

MAR-APR
1-2 INCHES
NATIVE

The flowers shown are only ¼ inch across. This plant is prostrate and grows primarily in areas with very low competition from other plants. On Jepson Prairie look for it along the self guided trail near Olcott Lake.

CWW

Vernal Pool Popcornflower
Plagiobothrys stipitatus var. *micranthus*

APR-JUN
4-8 INCHES
NATIVE

The flowers shown are only ¼ inch across. This small, delicate plant is a California vernal pool endemic. It can be quite common in vernal pools at Jepson Prairie. It prefers the deeper and wetter pools.

CWW

Solano Popcornflower
Plagiobothrys hystriculus

MAR-APR
4-8 INCHES
NATIVE/RARE

The flowers shown are only ¼ inch across. This plant was once throught to be extinct until taxonomists began looking more closely. On Jepson Prairie it can be quite common in the shallow vernal pools. Its nutlets have prickles.

CWW

Common Knotweed
Polygonum aviculare

MAY-JUL
2-6 INCHES
INTRODUCED

Common Knotweed is a frequent inhabitant in many disturbed areas of California. You may see it in a local vacant lot or even in your garden. The species consists of several varieites which may occur at Jepson Prairie.

CWW

Caraway-leaved Lomatium
Lomatium caruifolium

FEB-MAR
6-12 INCHES
NATIVE

Occurs in grasslands. Native Americans used the dried roots to make a flour from which a type of biscuit was made. Early settlers used the foliage as an herb to spice meat and pots of stew.

CWW

California Golden Violet
Viola pedunculata

FEB-MAR
4-8 INCHES
NATIVE

This is a perennial violet and has the largest flowers of the natives in this genus. The large yellow flowers rival any pansy that can be purchased in a nursery. Following a fire, the plants are particularly prolific bloomers.

DW

Cicendia, Timwort
Cicendia quadrangularis

FEB-APR
1-3 INCHES
NATIVE

This is the only yellow flowered member of the gentian family. The flowers are four-petaled and only ¼ inch across. It can be common in the grasslands of Jepson Prairie. The species name refers to the cube shape of the calyx in fruit.

DW

Yellow Carpet
Blennosperma nanum

FEB-MAR
2-5 INCHES
NATIVE

Occurs in moist grassland and vernal pools. Can be very common at Jepson Prairie, particularly on certain soil types. Pollinated by native, solitary bees (see page 24). Yellow Carpet has white pollen, which is unusual in sunflowers.

CWW

Smooth Tidy-tips
Layia chrysanthemoides

MAR-APR
6-10 INCHES
NATIVE

Common in shallow vernal pools and moist grassland. The white circle with yellow center is like a bull's-eye or target to guide the pollinating insects to the nectar in the center of the flower.

CWW

Vernal Pool Goldfields
Lasthenia fremontii

MAR-MAY
4-6 INCHES
NATIVE

Endemic to California vernal pools and very common in most vernal pool areas. Pollinated by native, solitary, ground-dwelling bees (see page 24 for additional information).

CWW

California Goldfields
Lasthenia gracilis

MAR-APR
2-6 INCHES
NATIVE

One of the most common grassland flowers in the Sacramento Valley. When John Muir wrote about his trip across the great valley, this was certainly one of the species that brushed his boots "as if wading in liquid gold".

DW

Rayless Goldfields
Lasthenia glaberrima

APR-JUN
3-6 INCHES
NATIVE

Occurs in vernal pools and other seasonally wet places. While the common name may imply that it has no rayflowers, close inspection with a handlens will reveal that it does have rayflowers, but that they are very, very short.

JJB

Brass Buttons
Cotula coronopifolia

MAR-MAY
4-6 INCHES
INTRODUCED

Native to South Africa, Brass Buttons have become widely naturalized in California. They occur on drying mud near marshes and the edges of vernal pools. Brass Buttons have no ray flowers.

DW

Blow Wives
Achyrachaena mollis

MAR-MAY
4-12 INCHES
NATIVE

Blow Wives are most commonly observed when in fruit. See page 35 for a photograph of the large, round ball of shiny white pappuses on the seed head. The photo at left shows the plant in flower.

CWW

Common Groundsel
Senecio vulgaris

FEB-MAY
6-12 INCHES
INTRODUCED

Introduced from Europe, Common Goundsel is very common throughout California. You probably have seen it in your garden or lawn. The photo shows both the flowers and the feathery parachuted seeds.

CWW

Smooth Cat's-ear
Hypochaeris glabra

MAR-MAY
6-10 INCHES
INTRODUCED

The basal rosette of leaves of Smooth Cat's-ear is often observed on mima mounds, particularly on the disturbed soils of Botta's Pocket Gopher mounds. Originating from Europe, this plant is common throughout the great central valley.

CWW

Gum Plant
Grindelia camporum

MAY-JUL
1-2 FEET
NATIVE

While this is a native species, it tends to prefer disturbed areas. All parts of the plant are very sticky (or shiny) in appearance. It generally blooms well after the annual grasses have dried and turned brown.

DW

Fitch's Spikeweed
Centromadia fitchii

MAY-JUL
1-2 FEET
NATIVE

Fitch's Spikeweed has hypodermic-like needles on the tips of the upper leaves and bracts. The hairs are gland-tipped and give off a distinctive aroma. Some species in this genus are called Tarweeds because of their stickiness and smell.

CWW

Yellow Starthistle
Centaurea solstitialis

MAY-OCT
1-4 FEET
INVASIVE

Yellow Starthistle is one of the worst weeds in California. Its deep taproot allows it to out-compete other species for summer soil moisture. Seeds can remain viable in the soil for at least three years.

CWW

Hop Clover
Trifolium dubium

MAR-APR
4-10 INCHES
INTRODUCED

Many non-native clovers were introduced during agricultural enhancement projects in the 1930's, and were intended to improve forage in grazing land. Hop Clover was probably introduced at that time.

CWW

California Lotus
Acmispon wrangelianus

MAR-MAY
6-18 INCHES
NATIVE

Note the single yellow flower above each leaf. California Lotus is scattered throughout the drier grasslands of Jepson Prairie. As with most members of the pea family, it sequesters nitrogen and enriches the soil.

DW

Birdsfoot Trefoil
Lotus corniculatus

MAR-MAY
6-18 INCHES
INTRODUCED

Most commonly found in mesic areas near Barker Slough and Calhoun Cut. Birdsfoot Trefoil was introduced during forage enhancement activities in the 1930s. It is common in irrigated pastures of the valley.

CWW

Bur Clover
Medicago polymorpha

MAR-MAY
2-6 INCHES
INTRODUCED

This is a European weed intentionally introduced to improve forage. The seeds form in small coiled burs which usually have spines. The burs attach to fur much like Velcro® and are thus transported from place to place.

DW

Seep Spring Monkeyflower
Mimulus guttatus

MAR-AUG
6-24 INCHES
NATIVE

Occurs in wetlands along the railroad tracks and near Barker Slough and Calhoun Cut and on the margins of some vernal pools. The red dots at the throat of the flower are a guide to pollinators.

MEH

Butter & Eggs
Triphysaria eriantha

FEB-APR
4-6 INCHES
NATIVE

Also known as Johnny-Tuck or Common Owl's-Clover, this species occurs in moist grasslands. It is a "hemiparasite" and derives at least some of its nutrition from parasitizing the roots of other plants. Note the lobed purple leaves.

CWW

Field Owl's Clover
Castilleja campestris

APR-JUN
4-8 INCHES
NATIVE

Endemic to California vernal pools. Common at Jepson Prairie in the shallow and intermediate depth vernal pools. Distinguishable from the related Butter & Eggs by the green, linear leaves.

MEH

Gold Nuggets
Calochortus luteus

MAY-JUN
8-14 INCHES
NATIVE

This bulb plant blooms late in the season when the grasslands are nearly dry. Calochortus are beetle pollinated and you may see several species visiting the flowers. Another common name for this plant is Yellow Mariposa Lily.

CWW

Fiddleneck
Amsinckia menziesii

MAR-JUN
1-4 FEET
NATIVE

Occurs primarily in grassland where the soils have been disturbed. At Jepson Prairie it occurs mostly along the roadside. Flowers occur in a coil or spiral, with the lowest flowers blooming first.

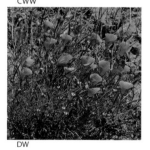

DW

California Poppy
Eschscholzia californica

FEB-JUN
6-18 INCHES
NATIVE

This is the California state flower. Several early settlers spread seeds throughout the state. Native Americans and early Spanish-Californians used a poultice made from the leaves and roots to make their hair shiny.

CWW

Filaree
Erodium botrys

FEB-MAY
1-5 INCHES
INTRODUCED

One of the earliest grassland invaders of California, probably from trash thrown overboard by sailing ships. Seeds are hygroscopic (attract water). They coil when it is hot and dry, and uncoil during the cooler evenings.

CWW

Cut-leaf Filaree
Erodium cicutarium

FEB-MAY
1-6 INCHES
INTRODUCED

Widespread weed of disturbed areas. Cut-leaf Filaree is especially common in areas with highly compacted soils, such as road edges. Another common name for this genus is "clocks" due to the coiling of the seed beak.

CWW

White-stem Filaree
Erodium moschatum

FEB-MAY
4-12 INCHES
INTRODUCED

Occurs in deeper soils than the other filarees. White-stem Filaree has pinnately compound leaves with oval leaflets in slightly unequal pairs. The seed pod beak is short relative to the other *Erodium.*

DW

Cut-leaf Geranium
Geranium dissectum

MAR-MAY
6-18 INCHES
INTRODUCED

Prefers open, moist, disturbed locations. Cut-leaf Geranium occurs most abundantly along sheep trails in the more mesic areas including adjacent to swales and vernal pools.

DW

Red Sand-spurrey
Spergularia rubra

APR-JUN
1-4 INCHES
INTRODUCED

The pink, five-petaled flowers are only ¼ inch across. Red Sand-spurrey occurs in disturbed areas and along road sides. It prefers areas with little to no competition from other plants and tolerates alkaline soils.

CWW

Italian Thistle
Carduus pycnocephalus

APR-JUN
1-4 FEET
INTRODUCED

Can be highly invasive in grasslands, especially in disturbed areas. In our area, Italian Thistle is generally a biennial. The overwintering rosettes shade the soil and prevent other plants from germinating.

JJB

Purple Starthistle
Centaurea calcitrapa

JUN-AUG
1-3 FEET
INVASIVE

Purple Starthistle can be highly invasive in soils with high clay content. Near Jepson Prairie, an eradication program using an herbicide similar to Roundup® during the summer has been highly effective.

DW

Purple Sanicle
Sanicula bipinnatifida

FEB-APR
1-3 FEET
NATIVE

Occurs in grasslands. Another common name is Purple Snakeroot. This is because of a Native American medicinal use in which a poultice made from the carrot-like root was used to treat snakebites.

DW

Sacramento Beardstyle
Pogogyne zizyphoroides

MAR-JUN
1-5 INCHES
NATIVE

Endemic to vernal pools of the great valley. Lavender flowers are generally less than 3 mm across. Can occur in both pools and adjacent moist grasslands. The plants have a strong minty smell, with chocolate overtones.

DW

Hyssop Loosestrife
Lythrum hyssopifolia

APR-JUL
1-6 INCHES
INTRODUCED

Plants with shiny green, opposite leaves and red square stems often observed in shallow vernal pools. The tiny pink, five-petaled flowers do not appear until after most of the other flowers have set seed and died.

CWW

Bluedicks
Dichelostemma capitatum

MAR-MAY
8-16 INCHES
NATIVE

This plant is a perennial bulb that occurs in grasslands. Most of the nutrient storage is underground. Pocket Gophers find these to be a favorite food. The flowers produce a pigment that can be used to dye wool a light blue color.

DW

Dwarf Brodiaea
Brodiaea terrestris

MAR-APR
4-8 INCHES
NATIVE

This perennial bulb-forming plant can be common in the Jepson Prairie grasslands. The underground bulbs are nutty flavored and nutritious. They are consumed by gophers and were harvested by Native Americans.

CWW

Elegant Brodiaea
Brodiaea elegans

MAY-JUN
12-18 INCHES
NATIVE

Blooms as the grasslands dry. It can be distinguished from the other Brodiaeas on Jepson Prairie by its relatively tall stature and the staminodes apppressed to the petals. Again, the bulbs are highly nutritious.

CWW

Alkali Checkerbloom
Sidalcea hirsuta

APR-MAY
6-18 INCHES
NATIVE

This annual occurs sporadically in the mesic grasslands on Jepson Prairie. The flowers can be pale to dark pink. Checkerbloom comes from the checked pattern of pale veins in the petals.

MEH

Checkerbloom
Sidalcea malviflora

APR-MAY
6-24 INCHES
NATIVE

This perennial occurs occasionally in the drier grasslands on Jepson Prairie. The flowers can be pale to dark pink. Multiple lax and sprawling stems can arise from a basal clump of shiny leaves.

MEH

Red Maids
Calandrinia ciliata

FEB-APR
3-12 INCHES
NATIVE

While Red Maids are native to California, they often occur in disturbed areas. Look for them in old fire breaks. Also known as "poor man's weather vane", they open only when the sun is shining.

DW

June Centaury
Zeltnera muehlenbergii

MAY-JUL
3-18 INCHES
NATIVE

June Centaury occurs in a variety of wetland habitats. In vernal pools, it is usually quite small and few-flowered. In marshes, the plants can be robust and have a large, open cluster of numerous flowers.

CWW

Windmill Pink
Silene gallica

FEB-APR
6-12 INCHES
INTRODUCED

Another common name for this genus is "catchfly" due to its sticky hairs that entrap small flies. Occurs occasionally in the grasslands on Jepson Prairie. Flowers are pale pink with whitish centers.

CWW

American Lotus
Acmispon americanus

MAY-OCT
4-18 INCHES
NATIVE

Soft, gray-green foliage is quite noticeable during most of the spring throughout the grasslands. Late in the season, tiny pale pink pea blossoms appear. The seeds are large and eaten by birds and burrowing mammals.

MEH

Winter Vetch
Vicia villosa

MAR-JUL
1-3 FEET
INTRODUCED

Originally introduced in California to augment the nutritional value of grazing lands. Vetches fix atmospheric nitrogen and store it in their roots. This enriches the soil which, in turn, can make it more hospitable to other weedy species.

CWW

Dwarf Sack Clover
Trifolium depauperatum

MAR-MAY
4-10 INCHES
NATIVE

Common in moist grasslands. When in seed, the individual flowers inflate (as shown) and resemble small sacks. Clovers are highly nutritious to grazing animals and many of the native mammals that occupy the grasslands.

CWW

Tomcat Clover
Trifolium willdenovii

APR-JUN
1-2 FEET
NATIVE

Tomcat Clover is a strikingly beautiful native. When in bloom, its large magenta and pink flowerheads often stand above the grasses. Its leaves are very narrow and serrated along the edges.

DW

White-Tipped Clover
Trifolium variegatum

MAR-MAY
4-10 INCHES
NATIVE

One of the loveliest of the California native clovers. This sweet-smelling species is found in shallow pools and swales at Jepson Prairie. The honey produced from these flowers is one of the best tasting of all.

CWW

Bearded Clover
Trifolium barbigerum

MAR-MAY
4-8 INCHES
NATIVE

Abundant in the shallow vernal pools on Jepson Prairie. The common name describes the long, soft hairs on the calyx lobes surrounding each of the flowers. The most obvious feature is the punchbowl-like bract below the flowerhead.

CWW

Rose Clover
Trifolium hirtum

APR-JUN
1-2 FEET
INTRODUCED

Rose Clover can be invasive in some areas of California. It readily colonizes disturbed areas and chokes out native plants. At Jepson Prairie, it is most commonly observed along the roads and in other disturbed places.

CWW

Smallhead Clover
Trifolium microcephalum

MAR-APR
3-8 INCHES
NATIVE

Tiny pale pink flowers are in a head less than ½ inch across. The shallow cup below the flowers is soft-hairy and has pointed margins. Commonly found in drier areas such as the tops of mima mounds.

JJB

Thimble Clover
Trifolium microdon

MAR-APR
3-6 INCHES
NATIVE

The tiny flowers can be pink to white. The less than ½ inch cup below the flowers is smooth and hairless. The common name refers to the flat-bottomed cup below the flowerhead. It resembles a fluted cupcake paper.

CWW

Notch-leaf Clover
Trifolium bifidum

MAR-MAY
4-10 INCHES
NATIVE

Small, annual native clover with pale pink flowers. There is no cup below the flowers. As shown in the photograph, when the fruit begin to mature, the flowers become reflexed. The calyx lobes are sparsely hairy.

CWW

Foothill Clover
Trifolium ciliolatum

MAR-MAY
4-10 INCHES
NATIVE

Small, annual native clover with pink to rose flowers. There is no cup below the flowers. As shown in the photograph, when the fruit begin to mature, the flowers become reflexed. The calyx lobes are toothed along the margins.

CWW

Alkali Milkvetch
Astragalus tener var. *tener*

MAR-APR
4-6 INCHES
NATIVE/RARE

While the flower heads look very similar to clovers, the leaves are pinnately compound. Each leaflet has a notched tip. Alkali milk-vetch is considered rare, threatened or endangered throughout its range.

DW

Miniature Lupine

Lupinus bicolor

MAR-MAY
4-12 INCHES
NATIVE

The smallest flowered lupine in California. A common and sometimes abundant component of the grasslands. This plant is noticeable for its palmate (palm-shaped) leaves and later for its large pea pods which hold the seeds.

CWW

Blue-eyed Grass

Sisyrinchium bellum

APR-MAY
8-12 INCHES
NATIVE

Blue-eyed Grass is a relative of the Iris. It is found only occasionally in mesic grasslands on Jepson Prairie, but is common elsewhere. Colonists used a tea made from the plant as a remedy for fevers and other ailments.

DW

Fringed Downingia

Downingia concolor

MAR-MAY
3-5 INCHES
NATIVE

This is the most common Downingia on Jepson Prairie. It can be distinguished from related species by the large maroon spot near the throat on the lower petals. The upper petals have a fringe when viewed under magnification.

DW

Hoover's Downingia

Downingia bella

APR-MAY
3-5 INCHES
NATIVE

This is the second most common Downingia on Jepson Prairie. It can form dense stands on the margins of Olcott Lake and in other areas. It has three very small purple spots in the throat and larger yellow patch.

DW

Folded Downingia

Downingia ornatissima

APR-MAY
2-4 INCHES
NATIVE

Endemic to California vernal pools. It can be distinguished from related species by the upper petals which curl to the sides and by the slight horn that grows outward from between the upper petals.

DW

Horned Downingia
Downingia bicornuta

APR-MAY
3-5 INCHES
NATIVE

Endemic to California vernal pools. This Downingia can be distinguished from related species by the two purple horns at the throat of the flower. Most Downingia are pollinated by native, specialist bees (see page 24).

CWW

Flat-faced Downingia
Downingia pulchella

APR-MAY
3-5 INCHES
NATIVE

Flat-faced Downingia can form dense, monoculture stands in areas near Calhoun Cut on Jepson Prairie. Note the three small purple spots near the throat along with the two larger yellow spots.

CWW

Cupped Downingia
Downingia insignis

APR-JUN
3-5 INCHES
NATIVE

This Downingia is most commonly observed in Olcott Lake and other playa pools on the Jepson Prairie. Because of its long anther column, specialist bees (see page 24) have have to hang upside down to gather pollen.

DW

Dwarf Downingia
Downingia pusilla

APR-JUN
1-3 INCHES
NATIVE/RARE

The flowers of this species are less than ¼ inch across. Unlike most of the other Downingia, this plant is not pollinated by specialist bees. There are both blue flowered and white flowered forms on Jepson Prairie (see page 36).

DW

Coyote-thistle, Button-celery
Eryngium aristulatum

MAY-JUL
2-6 INCHES
NATIVE

The photo shows the plant in bloom during the late spring and early summer. While this species of *Eryngium* does not get tall, it has sprawling branches and can spread to more than a foot across. (Also see page 23.)

CWW

Dwarf Woolly Marbles
Psilocarphus brevissimus

APR-MAY
1-4 INCHES
NATIVE

This is a California vernal pool endemic, shown here during the height of the vernal pool blooming period. Later in the season, the leaves will fully enclose the flower and the flowerhead will resemble a woolly marble.

CWW

Round Woolly Marbles
Psilocarphus chilensis

APR-MAY
1-4 INCHES
NATIVE

Round Woolly Marbles are endemic to vernal pools in the great central valley and interdunes in coastal areas of California. The species is less hairy than the Dwarf Woolly Marbles and somewhat greener.

CWW

Oregon Woolly Marbles
Psilocarphus oregonus

APR-MAY
1-4 INCHES
NATIVE

This species is common in many habitats in California including shallow vernal pools. The minute flowers are enclosed in tiny, hairy sacks in the center of the flowerhead. The long linear bracts dsistinguish this species from the others.

CWW

Hogwallow Starfish
Hesperevax caulescens

APR-JUN
2-4 INCHES
NATIVE

Can be abundant on mesic soils that shrink and swell during periods of dry and wet, respectively. The flowers are at the center of the spatula-shaped bracts. This plant is endemic to the great central valley of California.

Turkey-mullein, Dove Weed
Croton setigerus

APR-JUL
1-4 INCHES
NATIVE

While this is a native species, it generally prefers areas of disturbance or bare soils. The common names are derived from the fact that the seeds are a favorite food of many birds. This plant produces its seeds in the summer.

CWW

CWW

Water Pygmy-weed
Crassula aquatica

JAN-APR
1-3 INCHES
NATIVE

Pygmy-weeds are in the stonecrop family and related to succulents in the genera *Dudleya* and *Sedum*. Water Pygmy-weed is endemic to vernal pools. It has minute, translucent white or pink flowers very early in the season.

DW

Erect Pygmy-weed
Crassula connata

JAN-MAR
1-3 INCHES
NATIVE

Erect Pygmy-weed occurs in areas of low competition in grasslands. Note the very blunt-tipped opposite leaves that clasp the stem. There are usually 2 flowers per leaf axil and the flowers have four sepals.

DW

Moss Pygmy-weed
Crassula tillaea

JAN-MAR
1-3 INCHES
INTRODUCED

Moss Pygmy-weed also occurs in areas of low competition in grasslands. It has narrow, pointed opposite leaves. There are usually 2 flowers per leaf axil but the flowers have only three sepals.

CWW

Water Chickweed, Blinks
Montia fontana

JAN-MAR
1-3 INCHES
NATIVE

Blinks have slightly succulent opposite leaves. The most distinguishing feature is the nodding flower head while in fruit. It has three valves that open to expose a single, large, black seed (see photo inset).

CWW

Water-starwort
Callitriche marginata

JAN-APR
<1 INCH
NATIVE

Water-starwort grows and blooms while there is water in the vernal pools. It produces rosettes of floating leaves during the aquatic phase. The picture at left is after the water has receded. The seeds are planted in the drying mud.

CWW

Shepherd's Purse
Capsella bursa-pastoris

JAN-MAR
6-24 INCHES
INTRODUCED

While this plant does have small white flowers, most people immediately notice the flat, heart shaped seed pods. If inverted they resemble a shepherd's purse. Most common in the grassier corners of the pastures on Jepson Prairie.

CWW

Shining Peppergrass
Lepidium nitidum

FEB-APR
2-6 INCHES
NATIVE

This plant has tiny white flowers that are not readily noticeable. Its most striking feature are the lens-shaped seed pods. Because of its peppery-mustard flavor, it was used as an herb by early settlers.

JJB

Heckard's Peppergrass
Lepidium latipes var. *heckardii*

MAR-MAY
6-12 INCHES
NATIVE/RARE

Heckard's Peppergrass prefers grasslands on clay soils. It has an elongated spike of seed pods and does not have a basal rosette of leaves. The Jepson Manual, Second Edition, treats both varieties as synonymous.

CWW

Dwarf Peppergrass
Lepidium latipes var. *latipes*

MAR-MAY
1-2 INCHES
NATIVE

Dwarf Peppergrass prefers clayey and somewhat alkaline grasslands. It has a tight head of seed pods within a basal rosette of leaves. The Jepson Manual, Second Edition treats both varieties as synonymous.

CWW

Fern-leaf Plantain
Plantago coronopus

FEB-APR
2-6 INCHES
INTRODUCED

This plant has tiny translucent flower petals and large white stamens. The leaves are pinnately dissected. Fern-leaf Plantain prefers bare soils, disturbed places and other areas of low competition.

DW

Legenere
Legenere limosa

APR-JUN
3-12 INCHES
NATIVE/RARE

This vernal pool endemic plant prefers the deeper vernal pools. It can be found occurring where Rayless Goldfields and Pale Spikerush occur. At left is the more common self-pollinating form. See page 36 for the flowering form.

CWW

Little Spikerush
Eleocharis acicularis

MAR-MAY
2-4 INCHES
NATIVE

This diminutive, native perennial spikerush is relatively common on the margins of shallow vernal pools at Jepson Prairie. While it can reproduce by seed, it also spreads with creeping rhizomes.

CWW

Pale Spikerush
Eleocharis macrostachya

APR-JUN
1-2 FEET
NATIVE

One of the only perennial species that occupies shallow vernal pools. When aquatic, Spikerush is hollow to transport gasses to the roots. When terrestrial, the stems fill with pith to give the plants more structural stability.

CWW

Toad Rush
Juncus bufonius

FEB-APR
2-6 INCHES
NATIVE

Toad rush is a cosmopolitan species that occurs in temperate zones worldwide. It has many growth forms and has had many names applied to them. The photo at left shows the plant late in the season. Earlier the plants are greener.

CWW

Curly Dock
Rumex crispus

ALL YEAR
2-4 FEET
INTRODUCED

Curly Dock has minute purple flowers that are seldom observed. Most people notice the reddish-brown, heart-shaped fruits in dense clusters (see inset photo). It is found in disturbed wet places throughout the United States.

CWW

Little Quaking Grass
Briza minor

MAR-JUL
4-12 INCHES
INTRODUCED

The flower clusters resemble rattlesnake tails when examined with a handlens. While this grass is not native to California grasslands, its small stature and early blooming time makes it a "naturalized" member of the grasslands.

CWW

Silver Hairgrass
Aira caryophyllea

MAR-JUN
4-8 INCHES
INTRODUCED

While this grass is not native to California grasslands, its small stature makes it a "naturalized" member of the vernal pool grassland community. It does not out-compete native species.

CWW

Vernal Pool Hairgrass
Deschampsia danthonioides

MAR-JUN
1-2 FEET
NATIVE

This delicate, annual grass is endemic to vernal pools. It most often occurs in vernal pools dominated by Vernal Pool Goldfields (see page 40) where it forms a purplish-red 'mist' over the sea of golden flowers.

DW

Annual Semaphoregrass
Pleuropogon californicus

APR-JUN
8-14 INCHES
NATIVE

This is a native annual endemic to vernal pools and similar seasonal wetlands. This plant is easily recognized by its flat spikelets waving in the breeze like flags. It has floating leaves that shade out other plants (see page 23).

JJB

Meadow Foxtail
Alopecurus saccatus

APR-JUL
4-10 INCHES
NATIVE

Native, annual grass endemic to vernal pools. It has floating leaves similar to California Semaphore Grass (see page 23). In the photo, you can see the white pollen which is carried by the wind from plant to plant.

CWW

JJB

Six-weeks Fescue
Vulpia bromoides

MAR-JUN
6-10 INCHES
INTRODUCED

This is the most common of three annual fescues that grow in the vernal pool grasslands of Jepson Prairie. All three were introduced from Europe and are considered "naturalized" but not invasive.

CWW

Italian Ryegrass
Festuca perennis

APR-MAY
1-3 FEET
INTRODUCED

A native of Europe, this grass occupies moist areas throughout much of North America. The plant contains a substance that inhibits the germination of many other plants and can be found in dense monoculture patches.

CWW

Wild Oats
Avena fatua

APR-JUN
2-4 FEET
INTRODUCED

A native of Europe, Wild Oats is common in grasslands through the United States and Canada. At Jepson Prairie, this grass generally occurs only in areas with deeper soils, such as the tops of mima mounds (see page 14).

CWW

Soft Chess Brome
Bromus hordeaceus

APR-JUL
6-24 INCHES
INTRODUCED

This European grass is one of the most common in California grasslands. While non-native, it is not aggressively weedy. It is also a favored forage plant for cattle. Many native grassland animals also consume its seeds.

CWW

Ripgut Brome
Bromus diandrus

APR-JUN
1-3 FEET
INTRODUCED

A very coarse non-native grass that prefers deeper soils and disturbed areas. As the common name implies, this species is avoided by animals, both native and domestic, because it causes harm to their stomachs.

CWW

Mediterranean Barley
Hordeum marinum ssp. *gussoneanum*

APR-JUN
4-10 INCHES
INTRODUCED

This is one of the only Mediterranean grasses that can occupy vernal pools. It generally occurs only in shallow pools or on the margins of the pools where water ponds for the shortest period of time.

CWW

Foxtail Barley
Hordeum murinum ssp. *leporinum*

APR-JUN
1-2 FEET
INTRODUCED

This grass prefers deeper soils and disturbed areas. At Jepson Prairie it can be found along roadsides and other disturbed areas. The seed head has backward facing hairs that allow it to easily lodge in the ears of dogs and other pets.

JJB

Meadow Barley
Hordeum brachyantherum

APR-JUN
2-3 FEET
NATIVE

Meadow Barley is a native perennial bunch-grass that occurs in mesic grasslands and on the edges of vernal pools. The spike is quite narrow when compared with the other barleys present at Jepson Prairie.

CWW

California Melic, Onion-grass
Melica californica

APR-JUN
1-2 FFET
NATIVE

Onion-grass is so called because of the inflated parts of the lower stems. This is a native perennial grass that prefers drier soils. The panicle is narrow and has shiny, papery spike-lets.

DW

Purple Needlegrass
Stipa (Nassella) pulchra

APR-JUN
1-2 FEET
NATIVE

Purple Needlegrass is the official state grass of California. It is a perennial bunchgrass that can be common and abundant in some locations on Jepson Prairie. See page 12 for a landscape view showing Purple Needlegrass.

CWW

Medusahead
Elymus caput-medusae

APR-JUN
6-14 INCHES
INVASIVE

One of the worst rangeland weeds of California. This grass contains a large amount of silica (glass). It is not palatable to most grazing animals and creates a dense thatch that prevents germination of native plants.

CWW

Barbed Goatgrass
Aegilops triuncialis

MAY-JUL
1-2 FEET
INVASIVE

Barbed Goatgrass has been invading California grasslands for the last decade or so. It appears to be very adaptable and can occupy extreme habitats. It is generally unpalatable to livestock and cannot be controlled by grazing.

DW

Salt Grass
Distichlis spicata

JUN-AUG
4-10 INCHES
NATIVE

Salt Grass is common throughout Jepson Prairie, but is most easily observed on the dry bottom of Olcott Lake during the summer. This is a perennial grass that commonly spreads through underground rhizomes.

CWW

Colusa Grass
Neostapfia colusana

JUN-JUL
4-10 INCHES
NATIVE/RARE

Colusa Grass is a native and endemic to large, playa-like, vernal pools of the great central valley. The population in the eastern portion of Olcott Lake is one of only about 40 remaining. It is monitored annually at Jepson Prairie.

DW

Solano Grass
Tuctoria mucronata

JUN-JUL
4-10 INCHES
NATIVE/RARE

Solano Grass is known from only four vernal pools in two locations and is endangered. The population in the western portion of Olcott Lake has not been seen since 1993. At that time only two mature individuals were observed.

Vernal Pool Invertebrates

A vernal pool is a world of exceptional diversity and an ecological system of unimaginable complexity. The organisms which inhabit this environment come in endless form and color, and all are superbly adapted to the rigorous environmental conditions associated with life in an ephemeral habitat. The uniqueness of such a habitat often produces equally unique organisms of very limited distribution, such as fairy shrimp (page 61) and Vernal Pool Tadpole Shrimp (page 62).

The same ecological principles, such as transfer of energy from producers to consumers and on through the various levels of the food chain, operate in this short-lived environment as in other biological systems. The primary producers in vernal pools are generally grouped as phytoplankton, those microscopic organisms such as algae which can photosynthesize their own food. Next in the food web are the primary consumers, which feed upon the phytoplankton. Many groups of aquatic invertebrates are primary consumers, and in turn, they are fed upon by predators. Because vernal pools are seasonal and generally do not support fish, the top predators are frequently other aquatic invertebrates such as aquatic insect larvae (or birds). Scavengers are also well represented in the pool fauna, feeding on dead plant and animal material and thus completing the food web.

Since vernal pools are a temporary habitat each year, the organisms which occupy them have developed various mechanisms to survive the yearly cycle of flooding and desiccation. To complete their life cycle before the pools dry, most of the vernal pool inhabitants develop and mature quickly. To survive the dry heat of the summer, many produce eggs which are capable of withstanding desiccation and heat. Others may encyst or burrow into the mud before it dries. The winged adult insects usually survive by flying away to another source of water. Those inhabitants which have not completed their life cycle and are unable to encyst or leave the water are doomed to die as the pool shrinks through evaporation. The water slowly heats up, the oxygen level drops, and eventually nothing remains but moist mud, which rapidly dries out under the hot summer sun.

Water Scavenger Beetles are at home in vernal pools as both larvae and adults. Adults breathe by trapping air under their wings

A variety of unique invertebrates inhabit temporary pools of water. These creatures represent some of the most ancient forms of life. They evolved long before fish, the primary predators of permanent bodies of water. These invertebrates thrive in temporary waters (such as rain basins and mud puddles) throughout the world. The invertebrates most likely to be found at Jepson Prairie Preserve and which can be seen without a microscope are illustrated on the following pages.

Aquatic Earthworms
Phylum Annelida

2-4 inches

Aquatic earthworms are found in the mud around and in vernal pools. They resemble familiar terrestrial earthworms. Reproduction is usually asexual, but some species reproduce sexually. Lost or damaged segments can be regenerated. Aestivation is by adults encasing themselves in slime to prevent drying, and by heat and drought resistant eggs.

Aquatic Snails
Phylum Mollusca, Class Gastropoda

0.5 inches

Aquatic snails are found creeping on the mud or in the water. They can rise or descend in the water by changing the specific gravity inside their shells. Aquatic snails are omnivorous scavengers. They aestivate by burrowing into the mud, and then sealing themselves in mucus to prevent water loss. Aquatic snails can aestivate for up to three years.

Fairy Shrimp (*Branchinecta* spp.)
Phylum Arthropoda, Class Crustacea, Order Anostraca

1 inch

Fairy shrimp are restricted to temporary waters. The species found at Jepson Prairie filter feed on algae, bacteria and other microscopic organisms. They lack a carapace typical of most other crustaceans. They swim upside down using 11 pair of legs to move in a graceful, gliding fashion. While swimming, their legs also sweep up food and channel it into a feeding groove. Reproduction in the species found at Jepson Prairie is sexual, and the males and females are easily distinguished. The males have long secondary antenna (photo) for clasping the females during mating. The female carries her eggs in a brood pouch suspended behind her last pair of legs (illustration). Fairy shrimp aestivate by heat- and drought-resistant eggs called cysts. Some species of fairy shrimp are endangered. (See pages 18 and 30 for additional information).

DW

Male fairy shrimp. Note the long secondary antennae, often called claspers.

DW

Flipped over Tadpole Shrimp showing one of the brood sacks.

Tadpole Shrimp (*Lepidurus packardi*)   0.5-2 inches
Phylum Arthropoda, Class Crustacea, Order Notostraca

Tadpole Shrimp are restricted to temporary waters such as vernal pools. They feed on algae, bacteria, other microscopic organisms, dead tadpoles, frog eggs, earthworms and even fairy shrimp. They scurry along the bottom of the pool stirring up the mud to find food. An oval carapace covers the back and the two brood sacs can be seen on the underside between the shell and last pairs of legs (photo). As Tadpole Shrimp grow, their number of legs increases, and they must shed their carapace. These can be found floating on the surface of the vernal pools. The red color of the legs comes from hemoglobin–the same substance that makes oxygenated mammalian blood red. Reproduction is primarily sexual, with some parthenogenesis. They aestivate by eggs/cysts like the fairy shrimp. Tadpole Shrimp are endangered (see page 30).

Clam Shrimp (*Cyzicus californicus*)   <0.5 inch
Phylum Arthropoda, Class Crustacea, Order Conchostraca

Clam shrimp occur in temporary waters such as vernal pools and seasonal marshes. They filter feed on microscopic organisms. They row their antennae to swim. Their entire body is enclosed in a bivalve carapace showing clam-like ridges. Males die soon after copulation. Aestivation is through resistant eggs/cysts.

Water Fleas   0.2 inches
Phylum Arthropoda, Class Crustacea, Order Cladocera

Water fleas feed on microscopic organisms and detritus. The body, except for the head and antennae, is enclosed by a carapace. Swims by stroking antennae. Reproduction is primarily through parthenogenesis. Late in the season males appear and sexual reproduction produces the aestivating eggs/cysts.

What are Cysts?

Vernal pool endemic animals in the class Crustacea produce cysts that survive the long hot summers. A cyst is a living embryo encased in a hard shell. The shell helps the embryo survive the heat and dessication of summer. When the rain returns, the embryo can hatch out very quickly to begin eating, growing and reproducing. This is an advantage when your aquatic world lasts for only a few weeks or months.

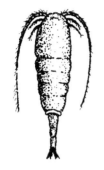

Copepods
<0.1 inches

Phylum Arthropoda, Class Crustacea, Order Copepoda

Copepods occur in all aquatic habitats and can be quite colorful, including bright red and blue. They feed on plankton and organic debris. They swim by beating their antennae and tails and then gliding. Females have one or two brood sacs, depending on species. Aestivation is by resistant eggs/cysts.

Seed Shrimp
<0.1 inches

Phylum Arthropoda, Class Crustacea, Order Ostracoda

Seed shrimp occur in most aquatic habitats. They feed on bacteria, algae and detritus. Their entire body is enclosed in a bivalve carapace without clam-like ridges. Most reproduction is pathenogenetic, but sexual reproduction produces the aestivating eggs/cysts. Some subadults may also aestivate.

Water Mites
<0.1 inches

Phylum Arthropoda, Order Acarina, Family Hydrachnellae

Water mites are related to spiders and ticks. They inhabit freshwater or are external para-sites on aquatic insects (often Water Boatmen, see page 65). They are generally bright red and swim by uncoordinated, but fast, flailing of their eight legs. They also crawl along the ground. Aestivation is by resistant eggs.

Springtails
0.1-0.2 inches

Phylum Arthropoda, Class Insecta,
Order Collembola

Aquatic springtails can occur in great numbers, resembling clouds of dust floating near the shore. When approached, springtails disappear by jumping very far and fast. They eat detritus, but little else is known about their life history. Springtails are the preferred prey of the Delta Green Ground Beetle (see page 30).

Dragonflies
adults 1-3 inches
naiads 0.75-1 inch

Phylum Arthropoda,
Class Insecta, Order Odonata

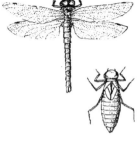

Both adult and larval dragonflies are ferocious hunters. Adults are terrestrial and hold their two pairs of wings outstretched to the sides. More robust than damselflies. They feed on flying insects. Naiads are aquatic and eat anything smaller than they are. Females drop the eggs on the surface of the water.

Damselflies
adults 1-2 inches
naiads up to 1 inch

Phylum Arthropoda,
Class Insecta, Order Odonata

Adult and larval damselflies are hunters. Adults are terrestrial and generally hold their wings together over their body. They feed on flying insects. Naiads are aquatic and have three leaf-like gills at the tip of their abdomen. They eat small aquatic animals. Females insert their eggs into emergent aquatic vegetation.

Aquatic Beetles
adults 0.05-1.6 inches
larvae 0.25-2.75 inches

Phylum Arthropoda,
Class Insecta, Order Coleoptera

Adult Predaceous Diving Beetles (Family Dytiscidae) are carnivorous on small invertebrates. Adult Water Scavenger Beetles (Family Hydrophilidae) are generally herbivores. Larvae of both families are often called "Water Tigers" and are predatory and cannibalistic. Both larvae and adults are fast swimmers.

Backswimmers

0.25-0.6 inches

Phylum Arthropoda, Class Insecta, Order Hemiptera, Family Notonectidae

Backswimmers have piercing/sucking mouthparts and feed on small insects, tadpoles and crustaceans. They swim on their back with rapid oar-like motions of their hind legs. Pale upper surface and dark underside. Adults fly from water body to water body. Backswimmers can deliver a very painful bite.

Water Boatmen

0.12-0.5 inches

Phylum Arthropoda, Class Insecta, Order Hemiptera, Family Corixidae

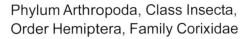

Water Boatmen have piercing/sucking mouthparts and feed on algae and microscopic animals. They swim with quick darting movements propelled by their hind legs. Males attract females by rubbing their front legs against their head, making squeaky chirps. Females attach eggs to submerged vegetation.

Mosquitoes

larvae 0.2-0.5 inches

Phylum Arthropoda, Class Insecta, Order Diptera, Family Culicidae

Larvae of the mosquito are called "wrigglers," referring to how they swim. They feed on detritus, although some are predaceous. Pupae are called "tumblers," describing how they tumble around in the water. Healthy, undisturbed vernal pools are not breeding grounds for mosquitoes. There are too many predators.

Midges

adults 0.05-0.4 inches
larvae <1 inch

Phylum Arthropoda, Class Insecta, Order Diptera

Midges are related to mosquitoes, but the females do not suck blood. The larvae are also similar, but midges generally lack hairs on the side of the head. They too wriggle through the water and eat detritus. Midge larve in the family Chironomidae are often red due to pigments in their circulatory system.

Amphibians & Reptiles

Most of the amphibians and reptiles found at Jepson Prairie occur in similar locations throughout the great central valley. The exception is the California Tiger Salamander, which is threatened under the federal and state Endangered Species Acts (see page 30 for more information). The most common of the amphibians and reptiles at Jepson Prairie are shown here.

Amphibians, such as the California Tiger Salamander and the Pacific Chorus Frog, breed in bodies of water and their larvae are aquatic. They are more successful when breeding in vernal pools because the most voracious predators—fish—are generally absent. They are eaten, however, by a variety of wading birds (see page 71). Before they can leave the water, the young must metamorphose from their aquatic shape to their terrestrial shape, complete with legs and internal lungs. If the pools dry too quickly, the current generation of offspring die.

Pacific Chorus Frog eggmass.

Pacific Chorus Frog tadpole.

Reptiles, including lizards, skinks, racers and snakes, are mostly terrestrial. They usually lay their leathery-shelled eggs in hidden locations or small burrows they excavate. The young incubate in the eggs until developed enough to break out and begin feeding. This reproduction is similar to that of birds. Reptile eggs are preyed upon by mammals such as the Striped Skunk (*Mephitis mephitis*) and other reptiles.

AC

California Tiger Salamander
3-7 inches
Nocturnal

Ambystoma californiense

California Tiger Salamander adults spend most of their time in mammal burrows. As adults, they eat insects and other invertebrates. For more of their life history see pages 20-21.

DR

Pacific Chorus Frog
1-2 inches
Diurnal

Pseudacris regilla

Pacific Chorus Frogs are active during the day, but they sing mostly in the evenings. Adults eat invertebrates. Larvae or tadpoles eat algae and whatever else fits in their mouths.

AC

Western Fence Lizard
3-8 inches
Diurnal
Sceloporus occidentalis

During breeding season, the male has a bright blue underside, hence another common name— bluebelly. Perched males do pushups to intimidate rivals. They eat insects.

AC

Western Skink
8-15 inches
Diurnal
Eumeces skiltonianus

The photo is of an immature Western Skink which has a distinctive blue tail. As they mature, the tail color fades to a dull blue, grey or rust. Skinks eat insects and spiders.

DF

Western Yellow-bellied Racer
20-60 inches
Diurnal
Coluber constrictor mormon

Racers are fast moving and highly active snakes. They eat small rodents, frogs, lizards and other snakes. If cornered they fight vigorously by biting hard and often.

AC

California Kingsnake
30-80 inches
Diurnal
Lampropeltis getula californiae

California Kingsnakes often hunt and consume other snakes, including venomous rattlesnakes. They also eat rodents, other reptiles, birds and amphibians.

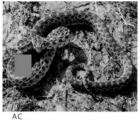
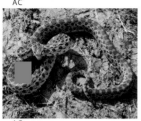

AC

Pacific Gopher Snake
40-60 inches
Diurnal
Pituophis catenifer catenifer

Pacific Gopher Snakes produce a loud hiss when agitated. This snake will also inflate its body, flatten its head and vigorously shake its tail. Diet includes rodents, birds and their eggs.

AC

Common Garter Snake
20-50 inches
Diurnal
Thamnophis sirtalis

Garter snakes secrete a foul-smelling fluid when handled or harmed. Their saliva is also toxic to small animals. Their diet consists of amphibians, earthworms, small birds and rodents.

Birds

To a casual observer, vernal pool grasslands may not appear to offer much to attract birds. There are few trees or shrubs in which to nest or perch. During the summer the land is parched and dry. However, there are numerous groups of birds that specialize in grassland habitats and even nest on the ground. These include seed and insect eaters as well as birds of prey. Other birds nest elsewhere, but forage in the vernal pool grasslands either seasonally or year round.

During the wet season, the vernal pools offer an opportunity for migratory waterfowl to rest and feed before completing their migration. This is particularly important today because most of California's great central valley wetlands were converted to agriculture over a century ago. Tender young plants and vernal pool invertebrates provide an important source of nutrition for these birds as they approach the breeding season.

Other avian visitors are opportunistic and use multiple habitat types. Waders visit many wetlands in search of their prey, which is often amphibian larvae or aquatic invertebrates. Large birds of prey will hunt in many habitats, but open grassland is very attractive to those who use heat or sound to detect their prey.

– Aquatic Areas

Jepson Prairie has both seasonal (vernal pool) and perennial (marsh, slough and open water) aquatic habitats. In the late winter and early spring, Olcott Lake often contains many species of waterfowl and waders and can be a delightful place to birdwatch. Later in the season, and year round, Calhoun Cut and Barker Slough are important habitat to the birds that feed on aquatic organisms such as amphibians and fish.

– Grasslands

Raptors hunt for rodents and other prey. Seed and insect eaters abound. The melodious call of the Meadowlark rings out over the landscape. Flocks of blackbirds alight to feed on insects. Be cautious of ground nesting birds (see photo at right).

– Other Habitats

There are a few areas of trees and shrubs on the Jepson Prairie in the remnant Eucalyptus grove and in riparian habitat along Calhoun Cut and Barker Slough. These provide additional habitat for birds that prefer trees and shrubs for perches and nesting sites.

Red-winged Blackbird eggs in the grassland. Many of the birds of Jepson Prairie are ground nesters. When you observe a nest, please try to avoid it.

SS

Pied-billed Grebe
13 inches long

The Pied-billed Grebe is a small brown diver of ponds, marshes and large vernal pools. They become completely submerged when they dive. Note the chicken-like beak with a dark ring, and the puffy white under-tail.

SS

Eared Grebe
12-14 inches long

Note the crested black head, golden ear tufts and long, slender neck. A common grebe that occurs in its greatest numbers at Mono Lake and Great Salt Lake where it feeds on fairy shrimp before flying to Mexico for the winter.

SS

Canada Goose
25-43 inches tall

This large goose builds its nests on the small islands in the western half of Olcott Lake. Several pair successfully raise their young at Jepson Prairie each year. The Canada Goose feeds on shoots, roots, seeds and insects.

SS

Gadwall
19-23 inches long

Male is dark grey with a black rump. Female is mottled brown. The underside trailing edge of their wings is white. Feeds on aquatic plants and animals by sticking its head down and its rump up. This behavior is called dabbling.

SS

Mallard
20-28 inches long

Note the glossy green head, yellow bill and white neck ring of the male. The female is mottled brown with yellow bill and feet. Mallards also feed by dabbling and spring directly from the water into flight.

SS

Northern Pintail
21-28 inches long

Male is slender with brown head, white chest and a long needle-pointed tail. The female is mottled brown and has a pointed tail. The Northern Pintail is another marsh duck that dabbles to feed.

SS

American Wigeon

18-23 inches long

The male has a pale grey head with deep green on the sides and a shiny white crown. Females are easily confused with those of the Gadwall and Northern Pintail. American Wigeons also graze in the grasslands.

Northern Shoveler

17-20 inches long

This small duck was named for its large, spoon-shaped bill which gives it a front-heavy look. Male has red sides and belly with a white chest and green head. The female is mottled brown with a big bill and yellow feet.

Green-winged Teal

14 inches long

Teal are small and fly in tight flocks. The male has a reddish head and a conspicuous, vertical white stripe near the shoulder. As with most ducks, the female is brown speckled, but smaller.

Cinnamon Teal

15-17 inches long

A small dark chestnut duck with a bluish-white patch on the fore edge of the wing noticable in flight. The female strongly resembles a Green-winged Teal female but is slightly larger. She hides her nest under vegetation.

Ruddy Duck

15 inches long

This small duck dives under the water for its food. Its main food source is small aquatic insect larvae that it strains out of the mud at the bottom of Olcott Lake. Ruddy Ducks (both sexes) can be distinguished by their blue bills.

American Coot

13-16 inches long

Coots are related to Rails. The American Coot is a dark grey duck-like bird with a black head and conspicuous while bill. It has white patches under its tail. It pumps its head back and forth when swimming. Males and females are similar.

SS

American White Pelican   8-9 foot wingspan

Huge, white with black primary feathers and an orange bill. Occasionally observed in large flocks flying in lines or circling high in the thermals over Jepson Prairie. They are on their way to the marshes and the bay to feed on fish.

SS

Great Blue Heron   4 feet tall

A large, lean blue-grey bird with long legs, neck and beak. While on the ground, the heron may extend or fold its neck into a "S" shape. The neck is held in the folded "S" shape in flight. Prey are similar to the Great Egret.

SS

Great Egret   3 feet tall

Also a large wading bird, the Great Egret is all white with long black legs and a long yellow bill. It hunts slowly and methodically in shallow water. Amphibians, small fish, crayfish and aquatic invertebrates are its prey.

SS

Snowy Egret   20-27 inches tall

A rather small egret with a black beak, black legs and yellow feet. Adults have a crest on their heads. The Snowy Egret is a frenetic feeder, rushing about and shuffling its feet to stir up food.

SS

Black-necked Stilt   13-17 inches tall

A tall, slender wader with long legs and a long beak. Note the color pattern of black above and white below, and the red legs. They wade in Olcott Lake to feed on invertebrates and small crustaceans. Sexes are similar.

American Avocet   16- 20 inches tall

Similar to the stilt above, but with striped back and wings and grey legs. During the breeding season the head and neck are russet. They feed by sweeping their bill back and forth in the water.

SS

SS

Killdeer
9-11 inches tall

Easily distinguished by the two black breast bands against the white neck, breast and underside. A ground-nester, the Killdeer is well known for its ability to distract predators away from the nest by faking a broken wing.

SS

Greater Yellowlegs
14 inches tall

A slim, grey sandpiper with a black, grey and white checkered back and bright yellow legs. It has a long, slightly upturned bill. It may be distinguished from the closely related Lesser Yellowlegs by its thicker, knobby knee joints.

SS

Black-shouldered Kite
15-17 inches long

Whitish bird with long pointed wings and long tail. Wings with black shoulders on top and black patch at the joint on the underside. Most often observed fluttering its wings while it hovers in the air looking for prey.

SS

Northern Harrier
18-24 inches long

This low-flying bird of prey glides over the grasslands at a height of about 6 feet and uses sound to detect prey. Males are grey and females are brown, but both have a prominent white rump patch just above the tail.

SS

Red-tailed Hawk
19-25 inches long

Most often seen soaring overhead. When it wheels in the sky, the red topside of the tail may be evident. These hawks detect light in the infrared range, essentially heat waves, and use it to locate prey concealed in the grass.

SS

Turkey Vulture
6 foot wingspan

A huge black bird with a bald and leathery red head. When soaring overhead, the wings appear two-toned and paler at the trailing edge. Turkey vultures are scavengers and provide important nutrient recycling by feeding on carrion.

Great Horned Owl

18-25 inches tall

A large owl with ear tufts or "horns". Heavily barred on the breast and with a conspicuous white throat patch. A pair has regularly nested in the Eucalyptus adjacent to the parking area at Jepson Prairie for many years.

SS

Horned Lark

7-8 inches long

A brownish ground bird with black sideburns, two small black "horns" and a black breast splotch. Walks around instead of hopping. Makes short, low-flying dashes in front of predators, visitors and vehicles.

SS

Loggerhead Shrike

9 inches long

A relatively nondescript grey, black and white small bird with a black mask. It sits quietly on wires and then swoops down to catch its prey. It is well known for saving its meal by impaling it, alive and kicking, on the barbs of a fence.

SS

Brewer's Blackbird

9 inches long

A common solid black blackbird of grasslands and other habitats. Often forages in mixed flocks with other blackbirds. Male has a whitish eye and purplish reflections on its feathers. The female is brownish-grey.

SS

Red-winged Blackbird

7-9 inches long

Abundant across North America. The California great valley race is unique as it lacks the yellow bar under the red shoulder patch. Although usually a resident of marshes, at Jepson Prairie they often nest on the ground (see page 68).

SS

Western Meadowlark

6-10 inches long

The buoyant, flutelike melody of the Western Meadowlark is "the sound" of California grasslands. You may find a male perched on a post singing its heart out while displaying a bright yellow breast with a black bib.

SS

Mammals

Mammals occurring at Jepson Prairie are predominantly nocturnal rodents. Observing them means searching for signs of their presence, such as tracks, droppings, nests, burrows, scratch marks and runways. The most abundant mammal at the Preserve is Botta's Pocket Gopher. Holes and piles of loose dirt are visible signs of this rodent. The runways of the seldom-observed California Vole can be seen in the taller grass. The most likely mammal to be observed is the Black-tailed Jackrabbit. An early morning visitor may encounter the Striped Skunk (*Mephitis mephitis*) returning to his burrow after a night of foraging. On spring evenings, bats prey on flying insects. Other sightings have included Opossum, Beaver, Coyote, Raccoon (*Procyon lotor*), and dogs and cats.

A series of Botta's Pocket Gopher mounds. The gophers seldom venture outside of their complex burrow and tunnel systems.

A beaver dam on Barker Slough. The beavers have been living here since a volunteer project in the 1990s resulted in restored riparian vegetation.

© John White

Virginia Opossum
Didelphis virginiana (Marsupialia)

13-37 inches
Nocturnal
Introduced

The opossum was first introduced into California in 1910. It forages for anything edible, plant or animal. Opossums have long slender prehensile tails.

© Dave Strauss

Botta's Pocket Gopher
Thomomys bottae (Rodentia)

8-9 inches
Diurnal

Botta's pocket gophers are strictly herbivorous and will pull plants downward by the roots to eat them in the safety of their burrows. Their burrows are also a haven for CTS (page 20).

DR

California Vole
Microtus californicus (Rodentia)

6-7 inches
Diurnal

California Voles eat a variety of non-native grasses. Little is known of their diet preferences prior to European settlement. Because of their abundance, they have many predators.

DF

Beaver
Castor canadensis (Rodentia)

~3 feet
Nocturnal

Beavers are known for building dams. They then build their lodges in the ponds they create. They use their powerful teeth to cut trees for building and for food.

SS

Black-tailed Jackrabbit
Lepus californicus (Lagomorpha)

~2 feet
Diurnal/Nocturnal

The Black-tailed Jackrabbit is the third largest hare in North America. It uses the same territory year round and eats plants. They feed at night, but also move around during the day.

DR

Coyote
Canis latrans (Carnivora)

30-34 inches
Diurnal/Nocturnal

Coyotes typically live in family groups. Only the alpha pair breed, but the other adults help care for the pups. Coyotes are carnivores and eat primarily rodents and other mammals.

Acknowledgments

This edition of the Jepson Prairie Handbook owes an immeasurable debt to the planners and contributors of the first and second editions, which served as a guide and the most important source for this one. Contributors whose materials were used as the basis of this edition are: Teresa Dellinger, Tom Griggs, Charles Higgins, Robert Holland, the late Harold Kerster, Jessica Martini, Kate Mawdsley, Robbin Thorp, Dan and Mika Tolson, and Carol Witham.

We are deeply appreciative of the late Jo Smith and the American River Natural History Association for permission to use over a dozen line drawings which first appeared in *The Outdoor World of the Sacramento River Region*. Other illustrations reused from the 1998 edition were provided by Susan Brewer and Mika Tolson. The Sacramento Valley Chapter of the California Native Plant Society gave permission to reuse text and photographs from the *Field Guide to the Vernal Pools of Mather Field*.

New contributors to this edition include Chris Searcy (California Tiger Salamander), Ben Wallace (Geographic Setting Map), Shane Waddell (Vicinity Map). The Jepson Prairie Docents Coordinating Team made valuable suggestions that guided the planning for this edition. Lars Anderson, Jane Hawkes, Jane Hicks and Greg Kareofelas provided important proofreading assistance.

Design and layout of the 3rd Edition provided by Carol W. Witham.

And last but not least, we want to thank the many talented and generous photographers who contributed to this colorful new edition: Nicole Byrd (NB), Dennis Briggs (courtesy of Robbin Thorp), Chris Bronny (CB), Jennifer J. Buck-Diaz (JJB), Adam Clause (AC), Ken Davis, Natalie DuMont (ND), Mal Evett (ME), Dave Feliz (DF), John Game (JG), Mary Ellen Harte (MEH), Greg Kareofelas (GK), James E. Lewis (JEL), Ellen McBride (EM), David Rosen (DR), Chris Searcy (CS), Sam Steiner (SS), Dave Strauss, Ted Swiecki (TS), Robbin Thorp (RT), Bud Turner (cover photo), Genevieve K. Walden (GKW), Ben Wallace (BW), John White, Doug Wirtz (DW) and Carol W. Witham (CWW).

– Carol W. Witham & Kate Mawdsley, Editors

Index

Index